THE MODERN Homestead Manual

by Skip Thomsen
and Cat Freshwater

Illustrated by Sharon Carson
and Skip Thomsen

Updated and revised
Second Edition!

OREGON WORDWORKS
Portland, Oregon

The Modern Homestead Manual

ISBN: 0-9625960-7-8

Second Printing

Skip Thomsen and Cat Freshwater

Illustrated by Sharon Carson and Skip Thomsen

OREGON WORDWORKS
P.O. Box 321091
Portland, Oregon 97281

E-mail: thomsen@mailbooks.com
Website: http://www.mailbooks.com

Additional copies of this book may be be ordered directly from our Website

Dedication

The inspiration for this book came from our country friends and neighbors--those who made it, and those who didn't.

We were always saddened when a family or individual tossed in the towel and headed back to the very environment they had sought to escape. We learned a lot from these folks, and from our own experience, as well.

The Modern Homestead Manual is our effort to share the knowledge we have gained in the years we have been homesteading. We hope that this book will help those who are contemplating the homestead adventure, as well as those who are already living it, to be able to experience it to their ultimate satisfaction.

We wish you all the best.

TABLE OF CONTENTS

	Dedication	iii
	Foreword	vii
	Introduction	ix
1.	Self-reliance	1
2.	Togetherness	7
3.	Money Matters	13
4.	The Year Before	23
5.	The Destination	31
6.	The Big Move	39
7.	Country Neighbors	47
8.	Homestead Kids	51
9.	Buying a House	57
10.	Building Your Own House	65
11.	Alternative Electrical Systems	77
12.	Our Own Electrical System	89
13.	Water Systems on Alternative Power	101
14.	Elaine's Chapter	139
15.	Equipment	151
16.	Vehicles	165
17.	Getting the Most out of Your Wood Stove	175
18.	Earning Your Keep at Home	183
19.	When Things Look Hopeless	191
20.	About the Authors	195
	Resource Guide	199
	Index	215

Foreword

The intent of *The Modern Homestead Manual* is to provide a firm foundation for the homesteading experience for those people seeking a new life away from the city, as well as to offer enhancement for those already living beyond the sidewalks and power lines. We aim to help our readers make the right decisions toward attaining their goals, and then refer them to the guide at the back of the book for resource material to achieve their specific objectives in each facet of their adventures into homesteading.

The number of topics covered, and the complexity of each, means that a book of this size couldn't possibly deal with each topic in detail. In preparing our Resource Guide we have researched the reading material to recommend what we have found to be the best available. Our goal in this research was to indicate material that is accurate and authoritative, that covers all areas of the subject, that is well presented with both text and supporting illustrations, and that speaks to both the novice and the professional in language easily understood by all.

Another thing we look for in any book is a good index. A reference book needs to be indexed in such a way that any topic can be found easily from several directions. All the information in the world doesn't do you much good if you can't find it.

Introduction

Many of us dream about moving back to the land, of going back to a simpler, more self-sufficient lifestyle. To too many of us, a dream is all it ever is. Of those who actually take the big step and leave the city behind to try and make a go of it out in the woods, only a few manage to pull it off with any degree of success. Why?

Why is the simple life so difficult to attain?

When we set off for a picnic with our family, we have to make certain preparations if the event is to be a success. At the very least, we ought to take along the food, right?

If we were to set sail across the ocean, our preparations would be a lot more involved and very much more important. The success of the trip, even our likelihood of survival, would clearly depend on careful planning.

Embarking on a successful adventure into homesteading requires even more planning than a sailing voyage, but many folks treat it like a picnic. While a sailing trip requires fairly extensive and very careful preparation, it is all pretty specific. Much of the information needed can be taken directly from the many how-to books on the subject.

Sailboats, regardless of size or rigging, have lots of things in common. Sailing hasn't changed much over the last few hundred years, and the rules, once learned, always apply.

Homesteading isn't nearly so specific. Since every individual's idea of "homestead" is unique and each person's experience with it will be different, there are few rules in homesteading. The requirements for "sailing" each are unique.

What we will discuss in *The Modern Homestead Manual* are the common threads that run through the fabric of all homesteading. These "basic rules" are few in number but enormous in importance. They are mostly born of common sense.

Homesteading can provide the most wonderful times in anyone's life. The statistics are clearly biased toward failure, however. We believe that we can help change those statistics. All of the folks we know who became disillusioned with their homesteading adventures had one thing in common: they either had not known or simply had ignored the basic rules.

The Modern Homestead Manual is our effort to make these basic rules available, and to encourage and help homesteaders to their ultimate satisfaction. To do this, we focus on two main areas vital to successful homesteading. First, we help define reality for those folks who are asking themselves, "Can we make this work?" Just what is it they want to do?

Second, we offer a nuts-and-bolts approach to homesteading. We show how to gain competence in the many skills that are essential to a self-sufficient lifestyle. Both the awareness of the new reality and the competence to achieve it are essential.

In addition to the philosophical aspects of making it work, we will cover in some detail the more tangible topics: alternative electrical and water systems, vehicles and equipment, heating alternatives, homestead business opportunities, and lots more.

A successful adventure in homesteading requires knowledge in many areas. Knowledge, not expertise. Expertise comes with time. "Self-sufficient" means just that: whatever comes up, a homesteader can take care of it herself. She doesn't (even if she could afford to) call the plumber when a faucet needs to be repaired. He doesn't need an electrician to wire in a new outlet or repair a broken appliance. A homesteader fixes cars, overhauls water pumps, builds houses, lays bricks, raises poultry, administers first aid as required, cooks, sews, gardens, cans, builds fences, repairs tractors, solders, welds, is familiar with the capabilities and the safety requirements of power tools, and much, much more. And of course, all of these skills are in addition to those required for earning a living.

Earning a living? Whatever happened to living off the land? Read on; we'll cover it thoroughly.

Why call it a "modern" homestead manual? Countless magazine articles and lots of books have been written on the subject of homesteading. Over the last hundred years or so, the term "homesteading" has evolved to a new meaning, and there are about as many interpretations as there are homesteaders.

To us, the modern homesteader is someone who strives for autonomy; to become as self-sufficient and self-confident as possible. We don't mean by this that all folks calling themselves homesteaders are automatically enrolled in some sort of world-wide self-sufficiency contest, either. Each person has to decide just how far he or she wishes to take self-sufficiency.

To some, self-sufficiency is nothing less than the ability to raise all of one's food, create buildings, clothes and furniture from salvaged materials, and to live with no electricity. To others, the meaning is far less strict, but no less meaningful. To us, "homesteader" might be the antithesis to "consumer." Even the term "consumer" implies that one only consumes: continually buys, uses up, and buys more. A true consumer gives nothing back to the planet in return.

A homesteader, on the other hand, creates, nourishes, and nurtures. A homesteader is a worthy steward to the Earth.

A modern homesteader does all of these things, and more. A person need not consider himself less than a homesteader because he chooses to make use of some of the better technology available to us all. One can operate in a world of high-tech and still be as conscious of environmental concerns as someone living in a tent.

We're all in this together, and sharing our ideas and experiences can be a world of help to all of us.

What you hold in your hand right now is the basis for a solid foundation, the source for a successful voyage, in your very own homesteading adventure.

HOW TO REPAIR TRACTOR

Self-reliance

What Do We Mean by Independence?

This philosophy of independence departs from the strict "how-to" to discuss some shades of "why." If parts of this discussion read like creeping paranoia, please remember that this is a deliberation of possibilities and options.

Independence comes in varying degrees and is modified by many factors. The most independent among us are those with no possessions, no bills, no mortgage, no maintenance, and whose only worry is where the next meal comes from. Few of us are willing to give up our favored creature comforts for that much freedom; but any of us can attain the degree of independence that suits us.

Governments, by their nature, discourage independence. Independent thinkers are notoriously difficult to govern. Our founding fathers--all independent men--laid the cornerstones of independence for all of us in the Constitution and the Bill of Rights. And since the Civil War, the United States government in all branches has been whittling away, with a well-honed blade, at the freedoms that allow us our independence. We have local laws and civil ordinances, and federal and state regulations out the wahzootie, each of which is expressly intended to curb our individual independence.

We have a public school system that is designed to keep us ignorant of our personal powers and to force us to rely on our leaders to solve our problems for us. (Ever wonder why so few of those in power allow their own children to attend classes in the public school system?) We have the communications media for in-the-home brainwashing if our public education missed any random personal thoughts. And we have professional sports to absorb and diminish our feelings of impotence in effecting our world.

Most of us are lazy. We appreciate the government's telling us what to do so we don't have to do our own thinking. We accept all the new rules and regulations as they come along because we know our government is doing these things for our own good. How many times have you heard that expression?

If you want to be truly independent, anytime anyone ever tells you, "This is for your own good," tell him, "Thanks, but, no."

How Do We Regain Our Independence?

From seat belts and helmets for motorcyclists, through what politically-correct terms to call things, to which deodorant will make us most acceptable socially, we are being told what to do increasingly. And the differences between recommendations (advertising) and requirements (ordinances) will become less distinct as the power-mongers continue to prove their omnipotence.

Short of full-scale revolution, how do we regain a degree of the independence promised us by our founding fathers? First we need to stop subscribing to the belief that we need other people to tell us how to behave. And we can begin by stopping subscriptions to newspapers, slick magazines, and cable television companies.

Why drop cable tv? Aside from avoiding the often-destructive programs we're offered, there is the consideration about coaxal television cable being capable of carrying signals out of your home as well as into it. If you are of the mindset that Government is always figuring out new ways to pry into our personal lives, that gets a little scary.

So consider the elimination of most establishment input from your life! Consider that most of what the media gives us is carefully prepared material that somebody wants us to believe. Instead, read some spiritual words of your choosing, or how-to's or even a good novel. When was the last time anything you read in the newspaper or saw on the TV news made you feel better about yourself or the world we live it? Limit your attention to that which is uplifting and positive! Begin thinking more for yourself, taking less advice from others! Positive thinking is one giant step toward sel-reliance. Another is a conscious and thoughtful inventory of where you stand in that area right now.

Are you a self-motivated person who does well with no supervision? Are you skilled in most of the areas that you will need to make it on your own away from the city? Can you deal competently with mechanical things, the things that need to be fixed when nobody else is around to help?

Can you improvise? Could you get the tractor running without having the right parts? Do an emergency repair on a water pump with whatever you can scrounge up at the moment? Are you prepared to administer emergency first aid to an ailing person or critter? Are you ready, willing and able to let the seasons and even the day-to-day weather dictate your activities? And do it all with a glad heart?

If consideration of any of these concepts puts you in a cold sweat, you need to become comfortable with them during your pre-move year, or you need to rethink your plan to move back to the land. You need to be especially clear about being self-motivated.

The Value of Common Sense

One of the most valuable assets you can bring into a homesteading experience is common sense. The more, the better. We've all heard the stories about the PhD who couldn't screw in a light bulb. Well, those people really do exist. Among the neighbors we sadly watched try to make it and finally pack it in were just such folks. Professional-types fed up with the rat-race, they had read just enough "homestead" literature to get them into deep trouble, but not enough to know what they were really up against. They sold everything they had, bought their piece of land and proverbial old pickup, and started leaning on their neighbors for everything. They had no common sense, because they had never found a need for it in their city existence.

They didn't make it in the country.

Another trait that successful homesteaders seem to have in common is the understanding that the price of freedom is responsibility. The price of the freedom from dealing with utility companies is the responsibility of maintaining your own alternatives to those utilities. The responsibility of raising your own food is the price you gladly pay for the freedom from having to depend on the offerings of a greed-driven food-marketing industry. These are the simple, visible examples.

Country-raised children, who by any poll can be shown to be more responsible than city-raised kids, get that way largely because they are brought up with responsibilities. Responsibilities are a part of life on a farm and in most rural environments.

Self-reliance and self-confidence are among the valuable qualities that your children will learn growing up in the country, particularly if you integrate them into the day-to-day development and operation of your homestead. No longer will Dad, and maybe Mom, too, disappear from their lives early each morning and return in the evening with just enough energy left to make it through until bed time.

The lessons learned by kids who are at hand during the development of a homestead are many and rich. Even if you move onto a ready-made farm, the education in self-reliance is there. Home-schooling, if you are into doing it, makes the whole experience even better. Everything that happens becomes a learning experience. Home-schooled kids don't need to be forced to learn; they are excited about learning, because the learning always has something to do with the real life they are living.

City-raised adults who are considering a move to the outback might still have some things to learn about the relationship between freedom and responsibility. One notable example is the relationship between the freedom of not having to live with the confines of a straight job and the responsibility of doing what's necessary to provide for a family. This is where being a self-starter becomes really important.

We had some neighbors, a family of three. The dad had this fantasy going about how quitting his job and moving out to the woods meant the end of responsibility. Whoopee! Except that the house on the property needed a whole lot of work before it would be habitable, a garden needed to be planted, a water system had to be installed, and on and on. As Dad sat around enjoying his fantasy, Mom fixed the house (with a lot of help from her neighbors) and planted the garden and accomplished everything else that needed to be done, including playing chauffeur to their school-age daughter. She carried the load alone for about a year, and then she packed up their daughter and split. Dad ran out of money shortly thereafter and he disappeared, too.

On the brighter side, we've also had neighbors who started out on a shoestring with not much going for them besides their own self-confidence and an unending desire to succeed. Against all odds, they have been out there doing what so many people only dream about: running a successful, productive homestead, and cultivating spiritual health. The difference? They knew the relationship between the freedom they sought and the responsibility required to attain it. And they had the independent self-reliance to make their dreams come true.

All through the rest of this book, you'll find the seeds of self-reliance. Plant them liberally!

Togetherness

Eye-to-Eye Perspectives

If you are planning to share your homesteading experience with a partner, the first step is to establish the move as a joint venture. Lack of togetherness can make or break a move to the country.

Togetherness and sufficient capital are another two make-or-break elements in this fairly radical change of lifestyle. You can overcome a certain amount of undercapitalization and other kinds of incredible odds if your togetherness is intact. But even the best-funded enterprise is not likely to survive a lack of togetherness.

How do you know if you're "together"? First, are you both looking at your future from the same perspective? Are you both excited about the prospect of leading a possibly more primitive life? Second, do your abilities complement each other's? Do both of you have sufficient skills and talents that one of you isn't going to have to carry an unfair share of the load most of the time?

During the ten years we lived on our 108-acre piece of forest beyond the power lines, we watched about a dozen families and individuals, young and old, come from the city to find new lives in the country. Including ours, only two of those families made it. Of those who didn't, some lasted a few years, some only a few months. Some of the marriages finished in divorce, and all of those who ended up disillusioned went back to the rat-race they had sought to escape.

There are several things that all of those who failed had in common. One was poor planning. Another, and a part of the poor planning, was undercapitalization; they ran out of money and had no source of income. But the biggest factor that the couples who packed it in had in common--whether or not they had children--was their lack of togetherness in their thinking.

It really is imperative that all members of the family agree that they are seeking the same new kind of lifestyle. We heard many versions of a basic disagreement. Often we heard them as part of our introductions to our new neighbors: "This is my idea of heaven but my wife thinks it's the pits." She'll have him convinced of it shortly, too. Or, "I've wanted to do this all my life and George here is just wonderful for coming along for the ride." But George already knows it won't work.

Sometimes the parents both loved it but the kids hated it. Or the parents and the little kids loved it and the teenager hated it. Or Mr. thought that kids should be raised on a farm and Mrs. thought that they would be culturally deprived, lonely, and forever dirty. The list is endless.

If you are absolutely certain that you are ready for a backwoods lifestyle and your spouse isn't convinced, don't bank on being able to change his or her mind later. The time for both of you to be convinced is before you make the move.

See Elaine's Chapter for another perspective that covers the basic tenets of togetherness pretty well.

Again, togetherness and adequate finances provide the cornerstones of a successful homestead adventure. With both intact, success is virtually assured. Shaky capitalization can be worked around, to a point, if the togetherness is there; but no amount of money is going to take the place of any missing togetherness.

Finding a Partner

But what if you don't already have a partner? What if you're ready to set out for the wilderness alone and you'd really prefer to have some company? How do you find an appropriate partner? We highly recommend the method we used to get together. It certainly worked for us.

Most people in the woods are there by choice. And many of us often prefer our own company to the company of those who like noisy, smelly, frenetic cities. But there are times--when the sap is rising, or when the sunset takes an hour and a half to shift from orange to deep purple, or when yodeling at the top of your lungs doesn't get it said--that it would be nice to have someone to share things with.

So where do you look?

If you're past the pavement, your chances for meeting people in grocery stores or laundromats are limited by the infrequency of your trips to town.

Haven't most of the potential companions you've encountered in bars made you feel really glad you were going home alone? You might well meet a like-minded person if you volunteer for a community or ecological project. But can you afford the time for volunteer work that will keep you away from home? If not, maybe your best bet is to try what we did.

Back in 1985, Skip ran a classified ad that read:

> "Aging Hippie, 48 years young, 200 lb, 6'4", bearded, entrepreneur, pilot, educated, happy, articulate, energetic, adventuresome, artistic/ creative, flexible, living in unfinished owner-built home in the woods with 8-year-old-son, seeks compatible lady. She would be about 30-45, young at heart and high in self-esteem, mellow, have a sense of humor! She would appreciate wilderness and city, kids and critters (might even have some of her own) and being treated as an equal. She would not be much overweight or into organized religion or tobacco. Photo appreciated...." followed by a blind box number.

Cat was then 38--halfway between 30 and 45. She figured she had all the qualifications he was seeking, while his ad offered everything she was looking for. She answered his ad.

After pages of correspondence and hours on the telephone, we finally met. Having decided that if this didn't work, nothing would, we got married. And so far (nine years later), it's working. Now we would like to share two lessons that we learned with our experience.

In the weeks before our first meeting, we took advantage of the security in our mutual anonymity. Our correspondence covered the things that truly interested us: our philosophies, our goals, our past actions and rationales, our success and failures, our desires, even our peeves and pouts. Some of our letters were over twenty pages long, sometimes two or three were postmarked the same day. We concentrated on the cerebral: appreciating the facets we were finding in each other and realizing how much we had in common. We did not meet in person until we had exchanged several hundred pages of letters.

Two Rules of Advertising

Until that initial face-to-face confrontation, there was no chemistry involved in our correspondence. There was growing friendship, trust, even anticipation, but no chemistry. All the emotional plays that people put themselves through when they get acquainted were absent. We were able to discover each other's depth and direction in our letters.

And that's Lesson Number One: by corresponding honestly before meeting, you will get to know each other very well on all the levels that get ignored when you both are putting on your best selves dating. And if the magic is there, you won't be disappointed when you meet.

Our astonished single friends decided that what had worked for us would work for them, too, and came to us for help. That's when we learned Lesson Number Two: write your ad yourself. There is much more involved in writing an ad than the words that finally get strung together. The order in which you list your attributes defines a part of you. The words you choose to name them also speaks loudly. The way you define what you seek says as much about you as your definition.

Nobody else can write your ad for you. The more of you you put in your ad, the more likely you are to find someone who is looking for what you have to offer. Even if you live and work in a well-populated area, advertising is still the best way to let the greatest number of people know about you. And the more people who know, the more likely that one of them is offering just what you are looking for.

So if you live out of the mainstream and are looking for someone to share your life with, write an ad. Select a publication that is most likely to bear fruit in your orchard. You might even find someone near you who is eagerly seeking a chance to homestead far from the crowds.

Addendum

Time passes, and as I'm doing the updates for this second printing, my calendar says September, 1998, so I suppose I ought to update this chapter as well.

Back in '94, Cat decided to pursue some dreams of her own, and we became single folks again. I want to point out that to me, this doesn't negate anything said in this chapter on togetherness. I have no regrets. I believe that everything happens as it should and we had a wonderful, exciting and productive eight years together, and much of what we accomplished, including this book, would have not been had we not been together.

These days, instead of newspaper "personals," we have many similar services on the Internet. They offer exciting possibilities, in that *because* they are computer-based, the screening possibilities are endless and the reach is global. One such Internet service has made possible another wonderful connection for me . . . and I do hope this one is forever.

All of the above suggestions hold for Internet personals just as they did for the newspaper kind, and it's always a good idea to be careful. There are a lot of terrific, honest, people out there and there are also some very needy and eccentric ones.

NANNY'S
DAY
CARE
S.C.

Money Matters

Money is a Four Letter Word

As reluctant as we are to admit it, money and independence *are* closely related. We know a lot of good ol' hippie-types who do not hesitate to tell us that we've sold out to the establishment for admitting such a thing, but (and we're about as much ol' hippie-types as they come) there it is.

It is not impossible to live entirely without money; there are those who manage to pull it off. They might live somewhere where they can exchange some work for the rent, or even move from place to place house sitting. They might be lucky enough never to be presented a tax bill, and might also be able to swap chickens or eggs for whatever they can't provide for themselves.

However, it takes a pretty sharp barterer to wheel-and-deal for doctor bills, insurance, auto or truck purchases, tires and repairs, and the other fairly spendy expenses we all seem to be faced with from time to time. It is possible. It's just not likely for most of us.

Bartering, the IRS, and Freedom

On the most basic level, there is little difference between bartering thirty hours of work per month in direct exchange for rent, and working for someone else for thirty hours for pay which you then exchange for rent.

What distinguishes the above two approaches is that you don't have to deal with the tax man in the direct exchange and you get a good feeling from sidestepping the system. (Disclaimer: What we mean by "you don't have to deal with the tax man..." is that you might usually get away without dealing with the tax man. Technically, we are all responsible for declaring to the Internal Revenue Service the value received in any barter and then paying income tax on that value.)

But what if you could earn twice as much money in thirty hours as the rent would cost you? Would you then be selling out to take the job? If the job involved something that you felt good about doing, you'd likely be more willing to go for it.

The freedom associated with no burden of home ownership is euphoria to some. Others of us want to own our home, however humble it might be.

Some of us just feel more grounded in our own digs than when we're living in someone else's space. There's a feeling of security that you get from living in your own home, particularly if you built it yourself and it's paid for.

These are decisions that each individual must weigh with her or his own conscience. Like that thing with the tax man.

Cash Reserves

There are people around who still believe that armed with a dozen or two chickens, an old Chevy pickup and a chainsaw, they can "go back to the land" and survive. We have read articles in various magazines that even support this fantasy.

A few years back, we wrote an article for one such unnamed magazine. The focus of our article was that it takes money to establish a homestead out in the boonies. It takes more money to keep it running. We went on to say that it was our distinct observations that undercapitilization--lack of savings and/or income--is one of the biggest causes for the failure of most homesteading attempts. The article also presented quite a few possible solutions. We'd been there and we had some experience to share.

However, the editors of the magazine edited our article to their taste. As published, it presented only the positive-sounding side of each topic. All demonstrations of the realities that face active homesteaders (as opposed to "wannabe" homesteaders) were edited out. We suppose their rationale was that they couldn't sell as many homesteading magazines to dreamers by reminding them of harsh realities.

We're not doomsayers. There are lots and lots of ecstatic homesteaders out there who started with precious little and are making it just fine. But they are the ones--the self-starters--who supported their dreams with reality and a lot of hard work.

Even if you move onto a paid-for piece of land with enough extra trees for the lumber to build your house and enough space to raise all of your own food, the tax man will still want his annual cut. Even if your income is low enough that you need not worry about the IRS, you still need to deal with property taxes. If you are making payments on your homestead, you will have to buy fire and hazard insurance.

And what if the kids get sick? Who will pay the doctor bill? Or buy gas for the pickup--not to mention tires, insurance, and repair parts? There will be things you have forgotten and events you haven't anticipated. You can count on it! In short, you have to have some income, no matter how self-sufficient your homestead is. That income can be generated from the homestead itself in a number of different ways; and from our observations, earning your keep at home is the best way by far. We'll go into ways to do just that in Chapter 18, Earning Your Keep at Home.

An essential part of your planning year should be spent methodically salting away the cash reserves that will make all the difference to your survival. This is serious business. More often than not, when we talked to would-be homesteaders who tossed it in and headed back to the city, it was because they had used up their savings, had no source of income, and were broke. They had not anticipated just how much money they would need to get their homestead going.

How much you will need in the way of reserves will depend a lot on whether you are moving into an existing, operating, out-in-the-boonies homestead or starting from scratch on bare land. Moving onto an existing homestead might not be much different from moving anywhere else. (See Chapter 9, Buying a House.)

Starting from scratch, on the other hand, means that you will be busy for as long as it takes to build your shelter and get your place into some sort of livable condition. During that time, wouldn't it be nice not to have to worry about having to generate income just to stay alive? And wouldn't it be terrible to have to quit working on your half-built house because you ran out of money?

A Sustainable Income

Independence requires that you have a dependable source of income. It doesn't need to be a great deal of money, but it has to be realistically aligned with your lifestyle. We've had neighbors who derived their income from all sorts of enterprises. Some worked at straight jobs in town (a thirty-two mile round trip), several were artisans who worked at their crafts at home and participated in country fairs to sell their products. One young woman used her commercial sewing machine to manufacture various products for sporting goods dealers. Another neighbor hired out to do dozer work for neighboring farmers and ranchers, as well as homesteading neighbors. And we operated a desktop publishing business.

Here on the Big Island of Hawai'i a surprisingly large number of local folks are artisans who do their crafts at home and sell in the many fairs and sales held on all of the islands. Of course, this is made easier by the healthy tourist industry here. But, the same opportunities would be available to anyone living within reasonable distance of any community that enjoys even a seasonal tourist business. If your chosen homesite is within a day's drive of a large, metropolitan area, you don't even need the tourists. Many medium-to-large cities have ongoing "Saturday Market" operations that are thriving, and most have seasonal "Renaissance Fairs" as well.

Homesteaders, by their nature, seem to be most contented when they earn their living at home. Maintaining a straight job in town means being away from the household every day, all day; and although some folks are able to deal with it just fine, that separation can take its toll. Again, it's a personal matter, dictated sometimes by necessity, sometimes by choice, and sometimes by whether or not there are little kids involved.

Having a job in town with a finite end-date is easier to deal with, especially when the ultimate goal is self-sufficiency at home. For example, a job that you'll need to keep for a year or two until you get your home business off the ground, can be gone to daily with a growing sense of accomplishment.

How Much is Enough?

Unless you *know* that you have some dependable money coming in on a regular basis, you will do well to assume that you will have no income for your first year. How do you determine a reasonable sum of money to set aside?

What will be your cost of living for the year? Don't skip anything here: land payments, property taxes, auto and home insurance (which you will probably be required to carry if you are making payments on your land), groceries, school supplies, limited medical emergencies, gas and car expenses--all, of course, added to the amount of money it will take to accomplish your first-year goals on the homestead.

Will you need to build, remodel, or finish your home, or any other structures in your plans? If you haven't already accumulated most of your materials and equipment before your move, what will it cost to buy them? And don't forget those things that you will have to hire out, like road-building, grading, well-drilling, etc.

After you carefully assemble your anticipated-expenses list, add it up and then--you're gonna love this--double it. This may seem a little extreme, but it isn't. You *will* need twice as much money as you thought you would. In addition to higher prices there will always be unanticipated expenses. To rely simply on the list of expenses you're sure of is unrealistic, at best. We can't stress it enough: having to pack it in because you ran out of money is the worst bummer.

What worked for us was to get most of the expenses out of the way during the planning year, while we still had an income and while we were in a better position to shop for the best prices. We knew that we would need a tractor and snow-removal equipment. We spent a good deal of time chasing down ads for affordable (read: old) tractors, and finally found a gem at a good price.

Then, using the arc welder we had recently bought, we built a six-foot wide, three-foot high snow plow blade that mounted on the tractor's hydraulic loader-bucket arms. The tractor also came with a heavy-duty, three-point mounted grader-blade, which proved indispensable for maintaining our half-mile of driveway. We invested just short of $2000 in the tractor and all of the attachments, and felt really good to have that piece of equipment bought and paid for ahead of time.

Another contribution to your peace of mind might be to pay your land payments ahead for a year in advance. Remember, if you are starting from scratch, you should not count on having any income for that first year or so.

It takes money to live, even on a self-sufficient homestead. If your goal of self-sufficiency includes providing for your every need on the premises, you will need money to get to that position. Plan your move very carefully, and allow yourself a cushion for the unexpected.

After the first year, you will have a pretty good feel for what kind of income you will need to keep your place going smoothly. If you have built your homestead around the concept of maximum independence, you might need very little. If you are going to be dependent on the outside world for a sizable portion of your needs, you will likely need much more. You will have to decide how to balance the trade-off.

There are many ways to establish and maintain a dependable income, some of which are discussed in Chapter 18, Earning Your Keep at Home. Your lifestyle and the degree of independence you desire will determine the amount of income you'll need.

Retirement Income

One of the best things any of us can do for ourselves and our financial security is to establish an ongoing income for the future. And one way to accomplish this that has worked consistently for generations is to own rental property.

Can we hear you asking, "Where do these turkeys get off suggesting we buy a rental house when we can barely afford to make ends meet now"? Acquiring a rental is a long-term consideration for sure, and right now it may seem as distant from your needs as flying to Mars. But believe these two things: the future will be here some day for sure, and you CAN acquire a rental property for practically no money out of your pocket.

Owning a rental property has several advantages. The most obvious is the perpetual income after the property is paid off. The not-so-obvious are the tax advantages and appreciation. And you don't have to be a high-roller to take advantage of the tax credits offered to landlords, either. If you have any regular income that qualifies as "reportable," you can use the tax advantages of a rental to lower the amount of the income on which you need to pay federal income tax. We'll get into the appreciation advantage later.

There are several ways you can become the owner of a rental. The simplest is simply to buy one. How? Again, there are options.

Rural properties are often sold on owner contracts and can be purchased with very small down payments, as long as the seller is convinced that you are good for the debt. A house that can be rented for an amount equal to or greater than your monthly costs (the payments you will have to make to the seller, plus the taxes, insurance, and whatever utilities you will be paying for) is a good investment.

Basically, the only money you will have invested is the down payment, and the rental income will pay off the house. At the end of the mortgage period (usually fifteen to twenty years), the house will be yours free and clear, and the rental will be your permanent income. Depending on your age at the time the contract is paid, this income could be very welcome when you no longer can--or wish to--work a five-day week.

Your investment is also to your distinct benefit during the mortgage period, even if the rent income is no more than your expenses. First, there's the tax advantage, for the IRS allows landlords to depreciate rental properties. The building itself and the furnishings are depreciated even if, in fact, the building may be going up in value through normal inflation. The IRS treats your rental as a business, so all expenses, including repairs, maintenance and depreciation, are deductible against your total income.

If you are lucky enough to buy a rental in an area of increasing real estate values, the rent you charge will increase over the years, but your payments and costs will remain constant, creating a further advantage to you. Over the period of an average contract, it is not at all uncommon for a property to double in value.

As an option to keeping the house as a rental, at or before the end of the contract, the house can be resold at its new, higher value on another contract, the length and terms of which meet your needs at the time.

And again, you have options. If there is still a balance owing on your original contract, you can pay it off with the down payment you receive when you sell the house, or you can pocket the down payment and just keep making your monthly payments out of the higher payments you will be receiving. Then when you finish paying off your contract, the total income from the new contract will be yours.

Options to buying a turn-key rental include buying a basket-case house (often available for NO down payment) and rejuvenating it into a desirable property, or building a rental from scratch. If you have the ability, the time and the inclination, building a house is the way to get the most bang for your buck. You will end up having a lot of time invested, but your cash outlay will be at a minimum, particularly if you build it on a corner of the land you already own. Of course, building from scratch presumes that you either have the necessary funds or are able to get a loan for the purpose.

In most cases, when a house you build yourself is completed, it can be mortgaged in such a way that the payments are substantially less than the rental income, thereby producing a positive cash-flow immediately.

Check the Resource Guide for a book outlining ways to get amazing buys on real-estate suitable for rentals.

To conclude, we cannot stress too much: money does matter. Finances and togetherness are two of the cornerstones of a successful homestead adventure. With both intact, success is virtually assured.

KITCHEN
BOOKS
MATERIALS
TOYS
MONEY
SKILLS
BATH

The Year Before

Real-izing the Dream

Many people dream for years about a move to the country, and then finally jump into it with a sudden emotional splurge. Perhaps they visited some friends who lived in the woods and were thoroughly inspired by the peaceful ambiance. Maybe they just read the right article or story that gave them the last push they needed to pack up and go.

As the sailing analogy in our introduction pointed out, your own adventure into country living, especially the start-from-scratch kind of country living, needs a better foundation than is usually provided by emotional decision-making.

You will do yourself a giant favor if you allow a year or so to get it all together before actually pulling up stakes and moving out. During that year, you can do the research necessary to decide on your new location, or to make absolutely sure that the place you've already picked out is *really* where you want to make your new home. Some visits to your intended homesite and to your potential new neighbors are excellent ways to accomplish this. (See The Destination in Chapter 5.)

If you are going to be building your own electrical and water systems, it is important to determine early just what you will need from these systems. The pre-move year is an ideal time for the required research and decision-making. Then you can proceed to designing the systems, locating the hardware at the best possible prices, and becoming thoroughly familiar with all of it. The chapters on alternative electrical systems, and water systems that will work with these electrical systems (Chapters 11, 12, and 13), discuss this in detail. The Resource Guide suggests the best reading material we have found for each specific area you might wish to study on each of these separate tasks.

Subscribe to Local News

A subscription to the newspaper of your new homesite is a valuable resource in several ways. Studying a local paper from day to day is one of the best ways to become familiar with not only the resources of that area, but with the attitudes and character of the local people as well. The letters to the editor of any paper will tell more about the local folks and where they're coming from than all of the "news" stories put together.

The classifieds will tell you how stable or itinerant the population of the area is: watch for the frequency of "moving" sales, and the number of homes for sale; seeing how long they remain listed in the paper will tell you much about the market. Classifieds can give you a good general idea of real estate values and trends, and offer bargains in tools, equipment, building materials and farm machinery. Most small-town papers have some variation of a "gossip" column, too. Local chit-chat about what's going on is a great source of information about the character of the community.

You might also start living a lifestyle closer to what you will be doing in your new environment. There's nothing like *doing* it to help you make some rational decisions about how you want it to work. And as Elaine points out in Chapter 14, there's a lot of value in putting new ideas to the test of time.

Lifestyle Choices

Many things that are genuine fun at first can eventually grow to be annoying inconveniences. Using your year-before to live with some of the actual changes you're considering will be essential to you in determining just how long they'll remain fun. For example, if you think that you would like living with kerosene lamps, try it for a while. No fair turning on an electric light when you feel like it. Live with *just* kerosene lamps.

There are nearly as many different lifestyles beyond the sidewalks as there are people living there. The range runs from very simple/primitive, with no electricity and only the most basic amenities, all the way to a homestead that is an all-electronic model of high-tech sophistication carefully built in harmony with its out-in-the-middle-of-nowhere environment.

Our personal lifestyle preferences call for a remote location very close to a warm ocean; lots of lush, green forest; no accessible utilities; and a basic, but comfortable, home with all of the electrical gadgets we like to live with, including a dynamite sound system, an office full of state-of-the-art desktop publishing equipment, and our completely outfitted workshop.

You get to decide just where on the scale from primitive to high-tech you wish to live. Diversity is one of the beauties of the modern homesteading movement. After all, how can you possibly get into a classic, stimulating, four-beer debate with someone who thinks the same way you do?

Locating What You Need

One of the more important projects of the year before is to accumulate most of the stuff you will need in your new environs. It is usually much easier to find good deals on tools and equipment while you still have access to city sources. (Classified ads, garage sales and auctions are all excellent sources.)

If you wait until you have moved onto your new place, you'll be busy with all your exciting new chores and when you discover you need something you hadn't thought of, you might not have nearby supply sources available. Even if you do find what you're looking for, you're much less likely to be able to dicker about the price if you have a pressing need. It's also easier to budget the purchases while you still have your regular income.

The concept of accumulating stuff also includes finding your building materials, particularly if those materials are not readily available near your new homesite.

During the year before our move to the mountain, we attended every farm auction we could, answered all of the building materials ads in the local (and some not so local) classifieds, went to garage sales, and made deals with several lumber yards on piles of odd-size lumber that had accumulated in a corner of the yard.

Lumber yards will often deal on stacks that have been around long enough to turn some of the lumber black. Since most customers reject the discolored stuff in favor of the nice, shiny, new supply, the old stuff just gets older. Yards will often sell it at a surprising discount--especially if you take the whole stack, and load and haul it yourself. Discoloration doesn't degrade the wood; on the contrary, the discolored stuff has likely been around long enough to dry out a little. And if it isn't warped yet, it probably never will be, unlike a lot of the new, green lumber cut from little, tiny trees.

Eventually, when our place started looking like our own lumber yard, we designed a cabin around the materials on hand. Rather a different approach from designing the building first and then buying the appropriate lumber, but it isn't a difficult process, and can yield really interesting buildings.

A note on buying lumber: rural communities often have lumber yards that deal primarily in lumber that is graded "utility." If you will be building a house that will be inspected during the stages of construction, discuss the use of utility lumber with your building inspector before you go out and buy any.

Unfortunately, as is the case with most things run by bureaucracies, the grading of lumber is both arbitrary and illogical. The quality of lumber often has little to do with the grade stamp. We have bought truckloads of "utility" grade lumber that was straight and true with tight knots. When we ran out and had to buy more from our local lumber yard, we got "construction & better" graded lumber that was crooked, warped, full of big knotholes; and not a stick had all four corners on it. But it cost twice as much as the tight-knot utility grade lumber.

We've bought stacks of lumber in which half was grade-stamped "#1" and the other half "#2." The "#2" was clearly better material. We one day watched an employee at a local lumber yard stamp "#1" on the better pieces of pine 1x12 that came out of an entire shipment bought as"#3."

Anyway, be careful. Though you might be able to buy better lumber for half the price, check with the building authorities first to see if they will allow it. Some building departments will also not allow the use of recycled lumber, no matter how beautiful and structurally superior it is to anything available today. Talk to your building inspector before you commit to any lumber purchases. You might just get lucky and find s/he is a reasonable human being.

The wisdom of locating and accumulating building supplies during your planning year depends somewhat on where your new home will be. If you are moving from a big city to a rural area not far from a farm-based town of some size, you might just do better finding your supplies in your new country environment. Look in your copies of the local newspaper and check the classifieds for the wealth of information on what is available and how much it costs.

Rural towns also often have auctions that feature goods rarely found in a big city. Do your research. Chapter 15, Equipment, will help you determine what you will need, and how to go about finding it.

Mastering Necessary Skills

The year before is also the time to take inventory of your skills. Your ability to achieve the self-sufficiency that is the dream of all homesteaders, is dependent on your skills. And common sense is the key to developing the many overlapping skills needed to be a successful homesteader. The skills come automatically as you undertake each new task and learn to master it.

Self-confidence, the knowledge that you can succeed at whatever you undertake, comes with undertaking lots of new challenges and not letting the occasional glitches get you down. Nobody does everything right the first time. Not even a turtle will get anywhere unless he sticks his neck out a little. The important thing is to try again until you get it right. An unsuccessful attempt is not a failure; it is a learning experience. Thomas Edison lost count after the first few thousand tries at inventing the light bulb.

During the year before you move, use every opportunity you get to learn new skills. And if the opportunities aren't presenting themselves fast enough for you, invent some. Help a friend with a project you've never dealt with before. Find a part-time job in a field that will teach you new skills.

Attend evening classes and college extension courses to tap into the variety of skills that are taught at evening schools. Among them are welding, electrical and plumbing basics, sewing, auto and truck repair, machine-tool operation, computer classes from novice to programmer, desktop publishing, horticulture, nutrition, emergency medical practices, carpentry, animal husbandry, small-scale farming, and many trade- and profession-specific courses. If you are unfamiliar with the schools in your area, check the listings in the phone book. If what you are interested in isn't offered, ask for referrals. Often private enterprises offer classes that relate to their own fields.

Are you going to be building your own house? There are a number of great books available that show how a house is built from the ground up (see Ch. 10, Building Your Own House). Or how about taking a job on a building crew to learn first-hand some of the tricks of the trade?

Thinking of making your own electricity? You should not only have all of the equipment together before your move, but you should know exactly how it's all going to work.

The same goes for water resource management or the handling of animals and growing of your own food. Read, read, read. And try to find reading material that will help you narrow your choices and define your needs. When you have decided exactly which way you want to go in any one project, then read the material that is specific to your particular situation.

A lot of books are vague and offer little more than theories about different ways to do things. You know the kind: you've read an entire book that promises to show you how to set up an electrical system, and when you're all done, you're more confused than when you began. Reading a lot of material that speaks of the alternatives available is a good way to get started, but when you have decided exactly how you want to handle a certain aspect of your proposed life, it's time to find *specific* instruction on how to do it.

How to handle what you want to do is one of the specific functions of *The Modern Homestead Manual.* In each of our topics, we cover the variables that are unique to homesteading, and then direct you to more specific reading to get exactly where you want to go.

There are few skills that go unused in homestead living. And no life we can think of that is more rewarding.

FOREST
BEACH
MOUNTAIN
PRAIRIE
DESERT
CITY
S.C.

The Destination

Decisions, Decisions, Decisions . . .

Let's say you and yours have it all together in the dreams and goals department. It's time for some constructive planning. First of all, where will you go?

Considerations in choosing your new location may include weather requirements, availability of water, access to maintained roads, proximity to nearest town and schools (not to mention the quality of each), local building regulations, proximity to relatives, and even such things as the political climate of your chosen state or locale. You might also want add a few items of your own to the list, and then sort them all out in order of importance. Any of these topics can influence the future success of your homesteading adventure.

In considering weather, you have several options available for making decisions. You can rely on published averages of high and low temperatures, snowfall, and rain. You can ask locals for their own evaluations; but be sure to ask several, because opinions vary widely on what constitutes good weather. If you ask a dozen or so, you can average out the answers for some pretty accurate numbers.

If it's practical for you to do so, visit your proposed destination during all the seasons and see for yourself. But because it's unlikely you'll be able to remain for much of each season, asking the locals will probably give you the best overall picture.

For various reasons, published figures rarely give you the real picture. For example, our homestead was only 16 miles from the nearest town, but there was no similarity between the weather in town and on our ridge. We were 2600 feet higher and a couple of ridges over from the Columbia River Gorge, where the published weather for "our area" was observed.

When we put our place on the market and were entertaining prospective buyers, we got a telephone call from a couple we were expecting. They were in a phone booth in The Dalles, our nearest town but down in the Gorge, yelling at us for bringing them to "this howling hell-hole" under false pretenses. We could not convince them that there was no wind on the ridge and the temperature was fifteen degrees cooler.

Weather patterns can differ significantly from one place to another because of topographical features, even if those places are fairly close together. The island of Kauai in Hawai'i is a good example. Both the driest and the rainiest places on the planet are within a few miles of each other. The whole island isn't very big, but one side has some of the lushest tropical rain forest you'll ever see, and the other side is a desert.

We recently lived four blocks from the ocean in Manzanita on the Oregon coast and we had studied the published weather picture before moving there. The nearest observation point was Tillamook, 25 miles south, and Tillamook held the state record for annual rainfall. But the sun was often shining in a cloudless sky in Manzanita when Tillamook was under a downpour or when, just a few miles inland on the other side of the hills, it was snowing.

Several visits during a particular year will tell you only what the weather is like on those days. In our ten years on the northeast slope of Mt. Hood, we had winters ranging from almost no snow and lows of 30 degrees, to five feet of snow and lows of 20 degrees below zero.

Availability of water can also be determined by talking to neighbors near your prospective new home. If wells are the normal water supply, ask about well depth, water quality, and well-drilling prices in the area. Again, ask several people.

Another good source of information is the local well-drillers, whose names can be found in the yellow pages.

In some areas, rainwater collected in a catchment system is the normal supply for domestic water. Our new home, the Island of Hawai'i, is a good example. We live at the dry end of the wet (windward) side and use catchment water for all our needs. The rainfall on the windward (Hilo) side of the Island is many times greater than on the dry (Kona) side. Many homes on the dry side depend on rainwater catchments as well, although some have to have water trucked in during prolonged dry spells.

If catchment is the likely system where you are looking, it's a good idea to get some accurate numbers on rainfall amounts and calculate these figures against your anticipated needs. Again, talking to the people who are already doing it is the best source of dependable information. When you approach with humility, most folks will be happy to share their knowledge with you. It shouldn't be difficult to find out how big a storage tank you'll need to make it through dry times.

Schools and Schooling

Many small communities have excellent school systems. There are still some maverick (good) teachers in the public schools, especially in the lower grades. Again, ask your potential neighbors. If they have any kids the age of yours, talk to them. You can get a good feel for a school by talking to the students who go there. Too often, a really good grade school will be followed by a less-than-mediocre high school, so check everything out that applies to your children. (See Chapter 8.)

If you plan to teach your children at home, find out what kind of community and local school support you can expect. Some communities appreciate home-schooling and will do all they can to help; others will offer to take you to jail if you don't send your kids to their schools. It's something you need to discover before battle lines are drawn.

Politics and Disclosures

The political climate of an area means everything from the state and local governments right on down to the individuals who live nearby. Get to know some of the folks who have been living in your prospective neighborhood for a few years. See if you feel comfortable in their company. If you are a cowboy, you might not want to settle in a town full of tenured professors of philosophy. Then again, you may want to honor those who also appreciate your chosen environment as much as you do, by welcoming them into your lives.

If you are considering settling in an established community, find out if there are any covenants and/or restrictions connected with home-ownership. Chapter 9 on Buying a House gives more specific information on covenants and restrictions which can range anywhere from vague and loosely-defined to very restrictive. Among the topics included are: how close to the road your home may be; what kind of septic system you must have; how tall your buildings may be; the maximum and minimum size allowed for a home; the (obscene) requirement that all building materials be new (as opposed to recycled); type, quality, and surface of your driveway; the need to have building plans accepted by a community-association review board; ad nauseam. And those cover just the tip of the proverbial iceberg.

Covenants aren't all bad, however. Some communities simply draft a master plan that will ensure the quality of life for the folks who live there. For example, the rules might include nothing more than restricting home-business ventures to those that are environmentally friendly: no excessive noise, odors or traffic.

In any event, do ask about covenants, restrictions and community associations, and follow up on the particulars if any exist.

If you find yourself talking to any realtors, ask several if there are any items of a general nature that need to go on federal disclosure statements when selling property in the area of your interest. For example, there might be a landfill that, as a newcomer, you might not know about, but that occasionally stinks enough to bother local residents. Something like that would legally need to appear on the disclosure statement.

Pay attention to the disclosure statement. A real estate agent may slide gently over the items on it, and in your excitement over the transaction at hand, the disclosures might escape your attention. You may regret the oversight later. If you later discover a local problem that does appear on the disclosure statement, you will have no grounds for complaint. But if a problem unfolds that was obviously known but not disclosed, you may have grounds for unwinding the deal.

It is important to discuss with local residents any disclosed items of which you are in doubt. Don't buy, move in, and find out later that the reason you got such a good deal is because nobody else wants to live that close to a chicken-manure processing plant. Be careful. This move represents your life, so talk to the neighbors, and not to just one. Some people like the aroma of chicken droppings better than others.

In our own case, the disclosure statement on the house we recently bought here in Hawai'i told of a nearby geothermal electric plant. Being rather hard-core renewable-energy enthusiasts, we thought that was great. After a very brief discussion on what a great idea it was to use the heat of our local volcano to generate electricity, the subject was dropped.

It wasn't until a month after we moved in that some of our neighbors started telling us about the terrible noxious emissions from the "geo" plant. Some claimed chronic respiratory ailments, others said that their chickens were dying. Yet others, who had been living here for ten or twelve years, said that they had never noticed even the faintest odor. We haven't either. The bottom line: be careful. Talk to the neighbors.

Building Officials and Other Bureaucrats

Whether you will be starting from scratch or doing any building at all, talk to the local building officials. Different areas have widely differing rules governing what can and cannot be done in construction. For example, in Oregon, it is now illegal to build a home on any land in "forest" zoning. And the land need not be adorned with trees for the bureaucrats to zone it as forest land. It need only be in an area in which someone with political clout doesn't want to see any homes; perhaps near a clear-cut where those in charge don't want to take a chance on getting sued by someone whose house they carelessly burn down with their slash.

It is to your advantage to get as much information as you can regarding allowable uses of the land in question. If you talk to the building department officials, be specific in announcing your intentions so that you won't be disappointed when you try to get a building permit.

For example, in some areas that might not allow residential use, a farm would be OK. If you can stretch the definition of your intended use to "farm," go for it. But don't buy a piece of land assuming that you'll be able to fool the building officials into thinking you are operating a farm just because you are raising a dozen or so chickens. If you are going to call your venture a farm, find out what the official criteria are for deciding if you do indeed have a farm.

Often, the size of a parcel of land can be a determining factor in land-use rules. If you are getting a lot of negative feedback from the planning department, ask whether or not it would work on a larger or smaller parcel of land. Sometimes, separating the acre (or less) that the home will sit on from the rest of the parcel will make a difference in both the feasibility of the project in the first place, and in the taxes later on.

If you are going to build your own home, check on the *current* local building codes before making your decision to buy the land. Building codes vary widely; and in today's pervasive climate of more and more laws, rules and regulations, it is not uncommon to see significant changes to building codes from one year to the next. The home you plan to build might not be allowed in the area of your choice. If we sound radical, it's only because we have been told we couldn't build as we wished. The long tentacles of bureaucratic intervention are reaching into some pretty remote areas of the country.

If you appreciate unusual building designs, one way to help protect your plan to build your dream house is to find a place where it is still allowed and build it as soon as practical. Next year might be too late.

If your property is well concealed and your bureaucrats are flamboyant nit-pickers, get your building permit for a pretty basic house, and when it's all signed off and the inspectors have finally gone, make whatever additions or alterations you see fit to make. But (disclaimer:) you didn't hear it here.

So, if you haven't already chosen your destination, give some thought to the points we've raised. And make your own lists of what you consider important. Check each thing out before you invest too heavily to withdraw.

WELCOME
SOLD
OLS
S.C.

The Big Move

Get Ready...

A lot of planning has brought you this far. You've likely been thinking about this move, adjusting to the awesome commitment involved, and preparing for this momentous day for a long time. Now, after a lot of intelligent research, you have found your new homesite. You've negotiated for a price that is fair to everyone involved, and the place is yours. You're ready for the Big Move!

The Big Move can take many forms. In complexity of planning, it can range from something as simple as a fifty-mile relocation to an existing farm with a turn-key house, to a cross-country move to bare land, taking along all of the supplies and equipment you'll need for your first year.

We won't dwell on the simple end of the moving scale; moving to anywhere with an existing house is pretty straightforward. Chapter 9, Buying a House covers this topic.

Since this move is intended to bring to you a degree of self-sufficiency, there will be planning involved that goes beyond that required for a regular move from one place to another. That planning will make it possible for you to have in your possession--before your move--most of the tools, equipment and supplies that you will need to see you through until you are thoroughly settled in. If you are moving onto bare land, your list should include everything you'll need to get your living quarters, electrical- and water-systems in place; plus building materials, unless they're as easily obtained near your new homesite.

When we moved to 108 acres of bare land back in '79, we moved only a four-hour drive from our existing home. Over the course of several months, we made many trips with our stout old pickup loaded to the limit with the building materials we had accumulated over the last year. On the last trip we made before our Big Move, we towed a borrowed trailer loaded with our tractor and all of its attachments. Everything else we owned (household stuff, tools and equipment) fit nicely in the 24-foot truck we used on Moving Day.

We were lucky that our new place was remote; its only access was a small road with a lockable gate. (Anything less protected might have made the security of our stash somewhat questionable.) If your new homestead doesn't offer safe storage for your materials, you have a couple of options. You might rent a barn or other building nearby. Or better yet, build a basic-but-lockable storage building on your new property, before the Big Move, so that it can be converted to other use later on.

A little neighborhood research is in order to determine how safe it will be to store materials on your new homesite. There are still places on this planet where people just don't mess with somebody else's stuff. But those places are getting increasingly difficult to find. Your new neighbors will be able to tell you how much you need to concern yourself with the likelihood of thieves.

...Get Set...

Another alternative to erecting a storage building is to purchase a shipping container from a freight company. These containers are all steel and very secure from all but the most dedicated thieves. One of our neighbors bought an 8' X 8' X 40' shipping container for about $1500, delivered to his site. Containers are not very pretty, however, so unless you have a permanent location where it won't be an eyesore, reselling the container after you are completely done with it would be the way to go.

A very important part of your pre-move planning was to accumulate enough savings to see you through until you start producing an income again. (See Money Matters, Chapter 3) One effective strategy we have used is to divert some savings into an investment that also solves many storage problems: a moving van.

All of the moving-van rental companies sell off their older vans from time to time. The bigger outfits usually sell their surplus trucks at dealer-only auctions and they must then be purchased from retail dealers. The smaller, independent companies often have older units for sale right on their rental lots. (If there are no "for sale" signs, ask. We've bought two that way.)

A good, used, ten- to twenty-year-old, full-sized moving van in excellent condition can usually be bought for less than $2500, sometimes for as little as $1000. You can rent a van for several hundred dollars and you will have to return it the day after the move, possibly to a city some distance from your new home. Or you can buy a van for, let's say, $2000. With your own van you can take as long as you need to load it. You can load it with the stuff you won't be needing right away packed way up front. When you get to your new home, you can take as long as you like to unpack, and use the van for storage for a few months, if you want to.

When you are finally done with it, you can sell it--probably for what you paid for it. We have never had a problem selling a moving van. Matter of fact, someone usually comes to us to ask if they can buy it when we're done with it, and we've always sold ours for more than we paid for them.

Rent a van, and you're *in* a hurry and *out* the rental fee. Buy a van, and you can take your sweet time, use it for storage, and your cost can be zip. The purchase money for the van shouldn't be a problem, because you would simply "borrow" it from your savings, and return it when the van is sold.

To give you an idea of how much fits into what size a space, in our most recent move we shipped all of our stuff in a 24' container (8' X 8' X 24', the same dimensions as a standard 24' U-Haul). Without wasting any space, we packed our household goods (minus appliances and large furniture; we left those behind), office equipment (two each computers, monitors, and printers, and a large photocopier, all in their original huge packing boxes; several file and other cabinets, desks and chairs), shop equipment (large woodworking machine-tools--the equipment took up fully one-third of the container), and the usual assortment of stuff one has around a country house: lawn mower, wheel barrow, garden tools, ladders, ad infinitum. . . .

Admittedly, we packed *very* carefully. Dresser drawers were filled to capacity with fragile goods packed in clothing, clothes were put in plastic bags and stuffed into odd-shaped spaces where nothing else would fit, and custom-sized bundles were made by carefully placing measured stacks of books into paper sacks.

This efficient, if fanatical, packing had a side benefit as well: since nothing in the container could possibly move, nothing was broken.

If buying your own moving van won't work for you and you need to hire a moving company, be sure to shop around for the best rate. Moving rates vary widely, sometimes as much as 300% for a single hauling job.

...Go

When you arrive at your new homesite, remember to protect the stuff you unload from the elements and from critters. We discovered porcupines by finding the damage they had done to some of our favorite furniture. They gnawed the legs off a fine, old coffee table and did minor damage to other pieces.

Tarps are OK for temporary rain and sun covers, but they won't even slow down rodents looking for something new and exciting to chew on. If you won't have ready storage available to protect your valuables, pack your van or truck accordingly: pack the stuff you won't want to deal with right away first. That way you can just leave it in the truck until you are ready for it.

Be especially careful with boxes of clothing or anything else made of fabric. Mice zero in on cloth as if they were trained for it. They can build an amazing condo in a box of clothes, and it doesn't take very long until everything in the box will have to be tossed. Boxes of clothing aren't even safe in your house, unless the building is mouse-proof. Field mice can get through cracks less than half an inch wide.

We spent a few weekends building a cabin before our Big Move. Our plan was to live in the cabin while we built our real house elsewhere on the property. As it turned out, the cabin just kept growing until it became a 1600 square-foot house. The "real" house never got built. We could have followed more closely our original plan if we had bought a good-sized travel-trailer to live in while building our house. Like a moving van, a trailer can be bought with savings and the money returned to savings when the trailer is sold.

Choice of temporary quarters hinges on several variables: the size of your family and their tolerance for less-than-comfortable conditions, the time of year and the weather, and the length of time you figure it will take to get your house liveable. Right now, we have neighbors who are living under a tarp while they build their home.

If your family includes kids, you'll need special considerations for them, too. Is there a school nearby, or are you going to home-school? Successful home-schooling requires some consistency in both time and place. And building an entire house presents them a wonderful opportunity for developing skills. You can give them projects to do that relate directly to the improvement of your homestead. Even a three-year-old can place little rocks at the edge of a path. Let them become a part of it, and they'll never be "in the way."

Plan your move to encompass the most favorable weather, figuring the time it will take to get your house weather-tight. A good rule of thumb is to carefully determine how long you think it will take, and double it (really! even if you're an experienced builder). If you're moving to cold country, remember that you'll wish you'd started building when it was still a little nippy if you're faced with racing to beat the first snow.

Additional Options

If you have an entrepreneurial nature, if you are good at and enjoy remodeling, *and* if real estate sales can be confirmed to be fairly brisk near your new destination, you might use some of your savings to put a down payment on a "fixer-upper" house. During the year before your final move, refurbish the house to the point where the profit from its sale will furnish a good portion of the capital you will need to build your own house.

This project can work from either end: the town nearest your new home, or where you live now. Ideally, do it in the better real estate market. The distinct advantage of doing it near your new home is that you get to familiarize yourself with the local folks in general and with building materials suppliers in particular. Depending on the circumstances involved, you might be able to live in the remodeled house while building your own.

If there is no electricity at your new homesite and you intend to develop your own electrical system, you no doubt already own the major equipment necessary to do so. The generator you will ultimately be using as a backup will work well to operate the tools you'll be using to build your home (and generator shed). Provide at least temporary but effective shelter for your electrical equipment. You won't want to have to repair weather-related damage to your equipment before even installing it in its permanent home.

Country Neighbors

Getting to Know Them

Making the move to independence requires thoughtful planning. We acquired several neighbors over the years who had not even considered that our winters often brought four or five feet of snow. Since we were the only ones on our ridge with a snow plow, we ended up plowing about eight miles of neighbors' roads for every mile of our own. We bartered this service for firewood.

Country neighbors are generally wonderful folks who are happy to lend a helping hand. Your own thoughtful planning will make it possible for you to become a good country neighbor as well.

It really is important to get to know all of your country neighbors. You will no doubt find that you have neighbors who live and think much as you do, and you'll also have neighbors who live in an entirely different world. You don't have to have a lot in common with a person to be that person's good neighbor. The essential ingredient here is co-operation. Matter of fact, we've watched some of the most interesting, if not downright unlikely friendships develop between our country neighbors.

It's heartwarming to watch rednecks and hippies learn over a period of time of helping each other out, that it's what's inside that counts, not what a person looks like, or whether he would rather weave baskets than herd cattle, wear sandals than cowboy boots, or ride a Harley rather than a horse. We've watched local ranchers and neighboring longhairs out mending fences together, helping each other with equipment repairs, pull each other out of the mud, and even get close enough to attend each other's parties on those warm summer evenings.

Things are different in the country. In the city, the rule of the day is: don't get involved. When a country neighbor gets in trouble, there's always somebody ready to lend a helping hand.

We've seen all sorts of examples of neighbors coming to the rescue. The problems? Among others, ailing livestock, a premature home-birth, tractors and equipment bogged down in three feet of mud, somebody seriously snowed in, a house burned to the ground, and construction projects needing lots of muscle.

Twice, a family moved in near us and needed to build a cabin in the few short weeks before our first anticipated snowfall. A half-dozen or so neighbors came over, tools in hand, and had a decent cabin up in less than a week. That's a welcome not soon forgotten.

Communicating beyond the Lines

When we moved onto the mountain, the nearest phone line was several miles away. Our first method of communication was a good old Citizen's Band (CB) radio. Everybody on the mountain had one, usually a unit designed for use in a vehicle, running off a 12-volt electrical system. CB's use very little power in "standby" mode, so we left them on 'round the clock. As primitive a form of communication as they were, they saved the day a number of times.

During particularly nasty weather, we made a point of keeping in touch with each other. We also had CB's in our vehicles, and when somebody took off for town during a winter storm, that person would get on the radio first to find out if anybody needed anything, and then announce an estimated time of return. That way, there would be folks paying special attention, listening for possible problems. Most town-runs were uneventful, but on the rare occasion that someone got stuck, help was always right there.

The big problem with CB radio is that it is the least effective in range and clarity during just those winter months when you need it the most. The winter brings the right kind of weather for the CB enthusiasts to "play the skip." The "skip" is a weather phenomenon allowing some radio signals to skip incredible distances, sometimes overpowering any normal signals in their path. Making matters worse is the fact that many of these enthusiasts increase their range dramatically with illegal transmitters that produce many times the power of legal CB's. During the winter, it was common for our local Oregon transmissions to be over-ridden ("stepped on" in CB lingo) by someone in Louisiana talking to someone in Alaska.

Two alternatives to CB's are radio phones like the ones used in trucks and taxis, and cellular phones. Both of these options are considerably more expensive to buy, set up and operate, but they are certainly more dependable.

The point of this discussion on communication is that the feeling of community that extended to our use of CB's (which we kept on line even after phone lines were run in) gave everyone involved a nice feeling of security: there's always somebody ready and willing to lend a hand.

How (and When) to be Truly Helpful

One more note on willing hands before we leave the subject. Let's say you can fix anything, crank out amazing amounts of work from sunup to sundown, and still spend quality time with the kids. You've planned your move well and have experienced no major glitches. You're out on your own and life is fine. Except. You have a neighbor who has trouble figuring out which end of the hammer is the handle. And he asks for help. Constantly. Now what?

Part of your task as a self-reliant homesteader is, of course, to be a good neighbor. And part of being a good neighbor is being helpful. But doing for someone else is not helping. Your neighbor needs to be independent, too. The best thing you can do for a neighbor so unprepared for his mission is to direct him toward learning how to do the task at hand. You won't be helping him if you do his job for him. You probably shouldn't even directly help him do it. If you are always ready to help him every time things get a little difficult, you are only enabling him to continue to ask for your help. If you show him how to do things himself, he will be much more likely to get in the habit of learning on his own.

Don't feel that to be a good neighbor you must always help every time anyone asks for it. Given the right (wrong?) circumstances, you might never get to spend any time at home. Who said, "Give a man a fish and feed him for a day. Teach a man to fish and feed him for a lifetime"? Well, she was right.

Last But Not Least

Country neighbors include the kids, too. Kids are always welcome and encouraged to join in with events, be they barn-raisings or parties. The following chapter on Homestead Kids, goes into some detail.

SODA
S.C.

Homestead Kids

Town and Country

The normal, contemporary city family often consists of a working dad, a working mom, and a youngster or two. The kid is trucked off to child-care, and is with mom and dad for a few hours each day and on weekends. The children are never involved with whatever it is that mom and dad do for a living; they are "gone" all day, every day, except Saturday and Sunday and holidays. In the evenings, quality time is hard to come up with because mom and dad are beat from the day's work.

The normal, contemporary country family is together a lot. Unless the kids are being home-schooled, they are away at school for the usual daytime hours, and except for that time, the family is together. Mom and dad work together to make their homestead work, and the kids are right there, not only able to see how it all happens, but to be a part of it. They are intimately involved in what makes a family run and how that family works within the community. From a very early age, homestead kids start developing that priceless commodity, common sense. They also learn that all-important value that many adults have never learned, responsibility.

Homestead neighbors spend time together socially and helping each other in various ways, again offering the children valuable experience. They learn about co-operation, sharing and helpfulness; they have opportunities to interact with other people of all ages, not just their peer groups.

Homestead adults seem to have a special feeling for kids, too. City kids are, for the most part, expected to go play with their peers and leave the grown-ups to themselves. Homestead kids of all ages just naturally become a part of whatever is going on.

Country kids learn responsibility at an early age, and it stays with them throughout their lives. They are integrated into the operation of the family in many ways, and from the time they can walk they can contribute. Thoughtful parents can usually find some worthwhile thing for a youngster to do that will give the child the opportunity to participate. Maybe it will be something as seemingly unimportant as spending hours putting little pieces of construction scraps into a pile for later use in the stove. No matter what it is, the child will have been a part of what was going on.

A lack of self-esteem is often the root cause of the suicidal tendencies of an alarming number of city-raised kids these days. As country kids grow, their participation becomes more viable, and they learn valuable skills while building self-confidence. That self-confidence brings with it a growing self-esteem, which is often the root cause of a successful life.

Tuning In

Country families are often found making music. Music seems to be a natural part of country life. Homestead kids participate in the making of music. To most city kids, making music means playing expensive compact disks on their expensive stereos and blasting their ears with loud, synthesized bass rhythms and lyrics which speak only of the futility of life.

The offerings of our cities that are denied to our homestead kids include screaming sirens, drive-by shootings, car-jackings, gang activity, a frantic pace, all sorts of destructive drugs, incredible peer-pressure, prejudice for its own sake, and the high-powered rantings of an advertising world that bombards us endlessly with the idea that whatever we have isn't good enough.

Country kids have to swap experiences like dropping quarters at the video arcade in the shopping mall for worthwhile and character-building activities like building a tree house, damming a creek, exploring and discovering, witnessing the cycles of nature including the birthing and dying of life and the daily wonders of sunrises and sunsets, and the sweet smell of country air.

Homestead kids learn priceless and enduring skills throughout their lives, and they learn them naturally when they are ready and eager to learn them. (See the Resource Guide for information on allowing kids to grow up naturally.)

The insane notion of keeping up with the Joneses isn't real important in the country. Peer pressure seems to be somewhat ingrained in human nature; but at least in the country, it is mostly limited to what is induced by TV viewing. Kids actually get to value each other for who they are, rather than by what labels appear on their clothes. And prejudice is limited to that taught by parents.

Achieving Education

Some folks listen to the propaganda delivered by the media and believe that the quality of our schools is as bad as it is because they need more money. They fear that the poorer country schools must then be hopeless. Money, contrary to popular belief, has very little to do with quality of education. Money only builds bigger, more powerful, and less effective administration machines.

Our country's academic records are an embarrassment. We spend more money per student on so-called education than any other industrialized nation. Our literacy rate is one of the worst. Our kids test at the bottom of the scale in just about all academic pursuits. Spending a few billion more on fancy real estate and high-priced administrators isn't going to help. Doubling the wages of an ineffective, non-caring, poorly prepared teacher isn't going to make him a better teacher.

New Zealand bears shining proof of the folly of the "more money" syndrome. Their country schools are all small, decentralized little-red-schoolhouse operations. The budgets of these schools often dictate that the local parents have to get together to do necessary repairs to the buildings and other things that need be done. Yet New Zealand's literacy rate is around 95%. Their country kids are bright, happy, articulate, and educated.

Check around. There are surely exceptions, but most small, country schools will surprise you with the quality of education they produce. We've seen many small schools where over half the graduating seniors go on to college and where more scholarships-per-student are awarded than at most city schools. The ingredients of an effective school are good teachers who love kids and working with them; parent participation with both the kids and the school; and kids who are eager to learn. All are in good supply at most country schools.

Home schooling is another option. Home schooling can be done on an individual basis, or several families can get together and the parents can share the workload of teaching. We have had the good fortune to know a number of families (including our own) who home schooled their children, all with excellent results.

Some school systems will co-operate with home schooling and even furnish books and other materials; others will not. When we started home schooling our son, the local school system came down on us with a vengeance.

They sent us all sorts of official-sounding letters claiming that they were going to force us to send Jake to public school because they were "concerned about his education." It took some legal research on our part to discover that because we lived farther than two miles from the nearest school-bus stop, we had the state's blessing to home school our child legally.

If home schooling sounds like a viable option for you, find some other folks in the area who are already doing it. Talk to them. They can save you a lot of research time, and you might even find a home-school co-op that you would like to work with. Your public school would probably be able to give you some names. If not, just talk to local parents of young children. If all else fails, place a "looking for home-schooling parents" ad in the local paper or on a community bulletin board. And check the Resource Guide for some good material on home schooling.

FOR
SALE

Buying a House

Check it out

This discussion wouldn't be complete without a look at some of the more important considerations of buying an existing house, whether it will be your home or not.

Almost any house purchase that involves financing will have to go through an appraisal. Appraisals can be thorough inspections or haphazard cursory evaluations, depending on the lending institution, state laws, and the appraiser. Even if an appraisal is required, you should really do your own examination as well, rather than to rely on even a "professional" appraiser's report for the actual condition of a prospective house. We have seen thirty-page, seemingly thorough appraisal reports that missed such serious defects as major dry rot damage in main supporting beams, a masonry chimney that had settled to the point where the lean was obvious from the street, and gross electrical and plumbing violations of both code and common sense.

The inspection we recommend assumes that the person doing the looking is familiar with basic construction practices and with the terms used to describe parts of a building. If you don't feel comfortable making these evaluations yourself, please take someone with you who knows what to look for. You are considering a major commitment here; better safe than sorry.

When you are about to pay your hard-earned money for a house, it is well worth your time to check hard-to-reach places like crawl-spaces and attics. The crawl-space under a house will reveal a lot about the care with which the house was designed and constructed. Look for concrete footings that are broken, cracked, or out of place; sags in main-support beams; rot and termite damage (especially in the lower portions of supporting structure); and damage caused by leaks under bathrooms, kitchens and laundries. Look for contact between wooden structural members and the ground, particularly in older buildings.

If you're in a cold-winter location, check the plumbing for freeze-protection. Look over any exposed plumbing and check for recently-replaced portions. Ask why they were replaced. Check the wiring for general neatness and code applicability. In a very old house, check the condition of the wire itself. In an open run of wire, try bending a section of wire a little. If the insulation cracks easily or flakes off at the bend, you are looking at a dangerous situation to leave and an expensive one to fix.

A look in the attic can reveal leaks in the roof, termite damage, sagging rafters, masonry problems where the chimney goes through; look especially for traces of soot, showing that the chimney leaks through from the inside: a very hazardous situation. Inspect the condition of the wiring here, too. Check also for adequate attic ventilation.

Outside the house, look especially at the lower portions of the building. Check for wood-contact with the ground. That's a likely place to find rot and insect damage. Look over the roof and rain gutters. Check all sides of the roof, too. It is not uncommon to re-roof only the weather-side and leave the not-so-bad side for later.

Inside the house, don't forget to look up. Check for water damage on all ceilings. Look over any recent paint-work, too. It might have been done to cover up water damage. If you suspect any particular place in the house, remember to check that area when you inspect the attic space with the powerful flashlight you brought along.

Check for signs of mold or mildew on interior walls. This is often a sign of water migrating through from a leak outside. Leaks like this often go unnoticed for years; there might be some major rot in the structure of the wall and floor below. Tap on the wall in and below the area of any visible mildew. Listen for a dull, hollow sound that is distinctly different from the sound of tapping on a wall known to be in good condition. Check the outside of the house, around windows, gutters, loose or broken siding and corners, for evidence of leaks.

In an old house, any settling can usually be found in the fits of doors and windows. Evidence of settling that is obviously very old needn't be a cause for concern. As long as the evidence shows that the house has been stable for a long time, the only problem will be cosmetic. We've seen a lot of old farm houses that settled quite a bit shortly after their construction, and they've been re-sided several times over their long, productive lives. The siding may have been cut a little funny to accommodate the crooked doors and windows, but they just gave the house character.

If you don't want to bother cranking up the furnace in the middle of summer, get the seller to sign an addendum to the sales agreement that the furnace equipment and any appliances that go with the house are in proper working order.

Check the plumbing for adequate water pressure. This is more important in older homes and in those with non-municipal water systems. Turn on a shower or faucet and watch the flow as someone turns on a faucet somewhere else in the house. A significant drop in flow indicates either a badly corroded (and stopped up) run of plumbing, a poorly designed plumbing system, or a pump too small for the job.

Ask where the water comes from. If it is surface water, has it been analyzed?

Recently Remodeled

"Recently remodeled" are ad words that should be heeded as a caution signal. Many people will try to make their home more marketable by doing what they euphemistically call a remodel. This process usually includes things like gluing inexpensive paneling on the walls, laying down bargain-priced carpeting and of course, applying a fresh coat of paint. Sometimes these tasks are tackled by an owner who really feels that his work will improve his house's condition; but other times the work is done to cover up traces of cracks, leaks, mildew, filth, and other problems.

Either way, the owner has spent time and money on something that he or she feels will increase the value of the house, when in actuality, the remuddle has likely *decreased* its value because it raises a question about what's under all the new paint, carpet and paneling. Since it's unlikely that you would have chosen the same materials for the face-lift that the owner did, his house would probably have been more attractive to you in its original "fixer-upper" condition.

Make a Low Offer

If you find a place that has been fixed up prior to sale, and you like it in spite of the remuddle, don't be afraid to put in an offer that's way below the asking price. Low-budget remodels are not generally highly desirable properties, and if the house has been on the market for any length of time, the seller might accept an offer that will surprise you.

Properties listed with realtors are not exempt from low offers either. When you find the place you're looking for, don't show your enthusiasm to the realtor. He is, after all, the seller's agent, and it is his responsibility to get the highest price for his client. It is also in his best interest to do so, as his commission is going to be a percentage of the selling price. If the realtor says that he can't present an offer that low, tell him, yes, he can. It's his job to present all offers to his client.

If possible, find out how long the property has been on the market. A seller with a fresh listing is not as likely to be receptive to a low offer as one who has had his listing on the books for awhile.

If the house you're interested in has been on the market for some time, tell the realtor that you'll consider it, do some calculations, and get back to him. Then, if you really like the place and have done a thorough inspection, make a list of everything you found that needs work. Show it to the realtor and make an offer of no more than 70% of the asking price of the house.

For example, some years back a neighbor advertised his house for sale for $50,000. We told him if he hired a realtor, he could get $60,000 for the place; but he insisted that he didn't want to pay a commission. The first people who came to look at it were two very nice little old ladies who politely told him that they didn't like the way the house was laid out, and that it wouldn't suit their needs.

He was so absolutely crushed that someone didn't like the beautiful house that he had lavished so much love, time and money on for forty years (it really was a beautiful place), that he reran his ad, only the second time at $30,000. The first person to respond to his new ad came to the door and asked, "Is this the place that's for sale for $30,000?" When he said it was, the guy whipped out his check book and wrote him a check for the full amount, on the spot. When asked if he didn't even want to see the inside of the house first, the buyer said that for that price, he didn't care if the house *had* an inside.

Contingencies

When you make an offer, you will be asked to write a check for $500 to $1000 as an earnest money deposit. A cardinal rule of making offers on real estate is to leave yourself an out. You may not need it, but there are all kinds of reasons that you might want to back out of a real estate offer. And most of these reasons involve things you find out after making the offer.

Have the realtor (or you do it yourself, if there is no realtor involved) include a contingency in your offer. If you simply decide to back out of a contract, you lose the earnest money deposit. But an unmet contingency lets you back out of a contract and get your deposit back.

Here's how it works. On the sales agreement (which is also the receipt for your deposit), you simply add a line that says, "this offer is contingent on the buyer being able to secure private financing," or "...being able to secure a building permit for the buyer's intended use of the property," or something similar. The financing line is a sure thing, because if you declare that your financing fell through (and it's real easy to not be able to get financing: just tell the loan officer you don't have a job) the contract is automatically void and your deposit must be returned. Of course, this presumes that the seller hasn't offered to carry the paper.

There is another use for contingencies, too. If you are unsure of anything that will be important to your use of the property, like being able to get a use or building permit, or a variance to put in a driveway where you want it, or perhaps securing written proof of timber or mineral rights that weren't available at the time you signed the agreement, be sure that these items are included as contingencies. Any statement made by the seller or realtor that is important to you and that cannot be substantiated at the time of offer should be made a contingency of the sale. That way you have the promise in writing, and your offer is void if the promise turns out to be false.

Read the Fine Print

Speaking of timber rights and such, make certain that on any rural property, there are no exclusions of timber, water, or mineral rights. Often, there will be an exclusion on a piece of property, and as the land changes owners through the years, someone will have left the details of the exclusion off the legal description. This isn't usually any kind of devious doing; more often it is because somewhere on down the line, a clerk copied the legal description from a document wherein the exclusion wasn't pertinent, and from that day forward it never got recorded again.

The best way to make certain is to go to the county courthouse and look at the records yourself. This is public information, and all you need to find the complete history is the legal description of the property. These histories are often quite interesting, too. You will learn when and how often the land has changed hands, who has owned it through the years, and how much they paid for it. In some cases, knowing how much the seller paid for the property can be a valuable bargaining tool, especially if he bought it recently.

If your search of the records shows that, for example, the timber rights were excluded on a sale of the property thirty years ago, unless another document to the contrary has been recorded since then, don't let anybody tell you that it doesn't matter. If the seller or the seller's agent insists that the timber rights are now intact, have them show you the legal document that makes it so, and don't settle until the document is properly recorded. It may sound like a hassle, but it's much easier to get it cleared up before you buy than to assume your rights for years and then find out that you have none. You're much better off to get everything cleared up before signing on the dotted line.

If there are any physical problems with the property that the seller promises to take care of later, insert a statement that if the problem is not resolved by a specific date, the seller must reimburse you for your costs in fixing the problem. Some examples of possible problems can include things like a large accumulation of rubbish on the property, useless equipment that needs to be removed, or even repairs that need to be made.

View Property

Are you willing to pay more for a property because of a wonderful view? Then make sure that your view will be permanent. Many so-called view properties are only view properties until the next house gets built in front of the current view, or until the trees between it and the view grow up.

The tree issue is often not so obvious, either. When we lived on the Oregon coast, we learned that most of the homes in our little village had once had an ocean view. The forty-foot tall pine trees that we loved so much when we moved there had all grown into the view within the last ten or fifteen years.

Look out over the existing view of any property you examine, look at the tree cover between the property and the view, and imagine what the trees will look like in ten or twenty years. Look also at any vacant land between the site and the view, and imagine what could be built on it.

Antique Houses

Don't be afraid of an old house just because it's old. There are lots of three-year-old houses that are infested with termites and have massive rot problems; and there are lots of hundred-year-old houses--even some built right on the dirt--that are solid as the day they were built. Old houses offer character, ambiance, and possibly even some local historical significance that can't exist in newer structures.

Older houses are also often not bank-financeable, so they are more likely to be offered with owner-financing. Owner-financing is always a better deal than working with a bank. The interest is usually less, the charges are significantly less and the hassles are infinitely less. We've seen cases where an elderly owner made a young couple an all-around excellent deal on a house just because he liked them, the respect they showed for his old home, and their expressed plans for maintaining his home's existing charms.

Speaking of charm, unless you sincerely love old houses and are willing to make the necessary repairs and maintenance that are often more difficult in an old building, you might want to rethink the whole idea. Newer buildings that are built to relatively modern codes and standards are usually easier to keep up and to repair. Older houses are usually laid out with small, separate rooms, unlike the large, open spaces found in most newer homes. Older homes are often drafty and hard to heat. Very few were insulated, although with standard stick-framing, insulation can be installed from the outside.

The point is, if you would be just as happy in a newer house, that's what you ought to look for. Old houses, like old cars and old people, require special attention. Unless you have a serious romance going on, they'll likely not get what they deserve.

Building Your Own House

Where to Begin

The logical first step in building your own home is to come up with a design. You can either buy a set of stock plans out of a catalog, or you can design your own home from the ground up. Since you're the self-sufficient type, you'll probably opt for your own design. If you want to follow the local rules, before you get too far along check with your local government to see if you need a building permit.

The days when you could go buy a piece of land 'way out in the woods, and just go ahead and build yourself a house are gone. Even if it's your land, you paid for it, it's big enough that your house will not be visible from anyone else's property, and the house is for you and your family, you may be required to go to the county building department and ask their permission to build your house.

A few years ago, the building code was in place mainly to insure that structures would be built to last; that joists and beams were of sufficient size to do their intended jobs. That's history. Now, mostly because of our country's flair for insane lawsuits and because of the legislative clout of the subsequently paranoid insurance companies, the building codes for most states try to insure that all buildings look like your basic, generic tract house. Oregon is a classic example.

We held a contractor's license in Oregon for years, and finally tossed it in when the building police decreed that we could no longer use the many skylights we had been using. That was the last straw. Our use of skylights created bright, airy and inviting spaces in our homes, even on the greyest of Oregon days. But as of 1992, the total area of a home's skylights is limited to 2% of the heated floor space of the house. Why? Because they said so.

In Oregon, the temperatures in the coastal areas rarely go above 85 degrees or below 35. In the mountains and high-desert areas of the state, the extremes go from over 100 degrees down to 40 *below zero*. Even so, the building police decided to make a state-wide energy code. The same amount of insulation is required everywhere in the state. Kind of blows their credibility somewhat, doesn't it.

If you live in a spot in the U.S. where it is still (more or less) legal to build a house on your own land without some bureaucracy's esteemed permission, you better get on with it before it's too late.

The UBC

Before you get serious about designing your house, you need to get a copy of your state's uniform building code (UBC). (You can sidestep this process if you are already familiar with general building regulations and the structure you plan to build is fairly conventional in design. Even so, it wouldn't hurt to get a copy of the latest addenda.) For most states, the UBC is from 1000 to 2000 pages of rules and regulations governing exactly how you must build your house--right down to how much room you must leave in front of the toilet.

The UBC will tell you how many windows you may have, whether or not skylights are legal in your area, how much insulation you must install and how and where you must install it, what your exterior doors must be made of, and all sorts of other details to stifle your creativity. Of course, the folks at the building department will tell you that the rules are not intended to stifle creativity, complicate construction, or raise costs; they are there to protect us. Too bad we don't have the option of signing a waiver that relieves the bureaucracy from its obligation to protect us in exchange for our freedom to make some of our own decisions.

Since the UBC is very expensive, you might wish to do your research at the library. First, find out when the latest revision was published, and make sure that your library has it. Drastic changes sometimes happen from one revision to the next, and there's no point looking at an obsolete book. In some states, many of the newest changes to the rules can be sidestepped by submitting plans that are signed off by an engineer or architect.

Building Inspectors

It wouldn't hurt at this point to go introduce yourself to your local building inspector. This is the person who will inspect your building as it progresses to make sure you're not cutting any corners and are doing everything according to local codes. Show him a rough sketch of the house you plan to build and ask if there is anything out of the ordinary that you should know about that might apply to a building like the one you're planning. If there are any unusual design features in your plan, make sure that they are easily recognizable in your sketches. Ask about any relevant recent code changes.

Some building inspectors are happy to help and encourage owner-builders. Others prefer to work with contractors who have no questions about anything, and they feel that owner-builders are a pain. And some areas of the country actually have a separate owner-builder code designed to be friendlier to someone who doesn't have the resources, skills and equipment available to most contractors. Be nice to your building inspector.

If your desire is for a more-or-less conventional building, one that looks like others in the area, you're safe to go ahead and draw up your basic house plans. Structures that include unconventional details like fabricated girders, unusual cantilevers, and such, will usually need to have the plans approved and signed off by a structural engineer or architect licensed in your state. This just means that after you draw up your plans, you will need to have an engineer or architect check them over, and if everything is in order and you've paid his fee, stamp them as approved. If you are particularly unsure about a certain detail you plan to incorporate into your structure, talk to the engineer first. It might save you having to do it over and pay him twice.

Permits and Easements

The next step is applying for (and getting) the building permit. In the blue-print package you submit with your building permit application, you will need a plot plan that shows exactly where the building will be on the property. Your research at the building department will have informed you of the setback requirements for your property. Setbacks are the distances any buildings must be from the property lines. On a parcel of land that is several acres or more, the set-backs aren't as important because you won't likely be building very near a property line anyway. On smaller parcels, the setbacks become more important. The front set-back is almost always deeper than the others.

Other considerations regarding where you may or may not put your house are easements. If your deed specifies any easements, look them over carefully for restrictions regarding building.

Some building departments also require a professional (read: expensive) survey to verify that your property is exactly as described in the legal description. Other information usually required on the building-permit application is the estimated cost of the building (on which your fee will be based), the names of the major contractors you plan on using, and the square footage of the building.

When you apply for your permit, you will be told how many sets of plans are required. Then all you need to do is submit the application, the plans, and the fee. Upon approval of your plans, you will receive your permit. If there is a problem with the plans, the building official will discuss it with you; and when it's fixed, you'll get your permit.

Depending on how things are done in your county's building department, re-submitting plans after corrections might be enough of a hassle that you will want to take every measure to get them right the first time. Some building departments will do a fix right on the spot, and others require another fee and more waiting until the right people can get around to checking your corrections.

If your building project will be using a septic system or a cesspool, the necessary permits should be obtained at the same time as the building permit. The building department official will direct you to the right places to obtain these permits.

Plans and Planning

Your plans should include a drawing showing all electrical facilities, including the locations of all outlets, light fixtures, refrigerator, disposal, dishwasher, water heater, etc. A copy of this drawing is what you will use to secure bids from electricians if you will not be doing your own wiring. You should send out (at least three) requests for bids right away, because if you need to hire an electrician, you'll need to start working with him very soon.

The plans will also show the locations of all plumbing fixtures including tubs, showers, toilets, and anything else that will have plumbing running to it. This is the drawing you will use to get bids from plumbers, if applicable. Again, these bid requests should go out even before you start construction so you can count on having the plumber there when you need him.

Some states do not allow us mere mortals to plumb or wire our own homes. You can save great gobs of money by plumbing and wiring your own house, and if you are capable of building a house, you are also capable of wiring and plumbing. We're not recommending that you avoid complying with your local regulations, but that you do as much of the work as is legal and practical.

By all means, if you are unfamiliar with these skills and the books we recommend still leave you less than clear on the subject, don't hesitate to enlist the aid of someone knowledgeable to help. On the electrical end, it may be possible to hire an electrician to make the final panel connections for you after you have run all the wires and installed the boxes. Again, ask around. There might even be a retired electrician available who would like to earn a few bucks.

Should You Hire a Contractor?

With your building permit in hand, you have several options when building your own home: you can contract the whole job out and stand back and watch someone else do the work; you can be your own contractor; or you can do the whole job yourself, hiring only what help you need as you need it. Any time you get a subcontractor to do a phase of your construction, he will generally be the one to secure any necessary permits and inspections.

Being your own contractor involves planning out the job from start to finish; locating and hiring the subcontractors and crews that will do the actual work; overseeing the work as it progresses; obtaining bids on and ordering the materials, and making sure that the right stuff arrives in the right place at the right time; making sure that all workers, subcontractors, and materials suppliers are paid in a timely manner; and doing all of the paperwork.

The paperwork includes getting estimates from subcontractors and materials suppliers; coordinating lenders (if any) with payroll, contractor and supplier billings; paying bills in general; making certain that everyone's license, workmen's compensation insurance, and bond requirements are met and in order; securing necessary permits; ordering the services for temporary electrical hookups, water hookup, sewer excavation and connection, inspections as they come due (excavation, foundation, subfloor, rough framing, electrical, plumbing, mechanical, and finals); keeping track of costs and comparing invoices with estimates, etc.; and finally, posting or filing notices of completion, and whatever other final documents are required by your county/bank/state.

The general contractor also gets to deal with the day-to-day problems that arise during the construction of any building: added materials for unanticipated changes, sending back the unit of plywood sheathing that was delivered 1/4" out of square, constantly staying on top of subcontractors so that they do their job as per schedule and so won't be in the way of the next sub who comes in, calling about orders shipped wrong or not at all, and so on.

Owner-Builder Options

Now, you might think that we're trying to talk you right out of acting as your own contractor. Not at all. We're just trying to let you know in advance what to expect. If you feel competent to handle the job, go for it. It pays very well. The general contractor earns a big fee for his work. You can pocket that fee, but you'll have to work for it.

Actually, being your own contractor is not so very different from being an owner-builder; the main difference is that an owner-builder does most of the labor. Another difference is that doing the work yourself means you won't have the responsibility of dealing with and co-ordinating subcontractors, unless you choose to or they are required by law.

The nice part about doing it yourself is that not only do you avoid having to pay for the contractor's efforts, but you'll be intimately involved with the project. And when it's completed exactly the way you want it, you get--rightly--to assume the credit for a job well done.

Be careful when hiring friends or local help to assist you. Be advised that you can get them into trouble. Some states have now made it illegal for you to hire anyone who doesn't have a license to do whatever it is he's doing, be it driving nails, landscaping your yard or cleaning windows. Usually, it's the helper who gets in trouble with the state's contractor's board, and he will be fined and forced to buy a license and bond. (Again, the bureaucracy tells us that this is done to protect us.) Of course, he can also choose to ignore the demands and go on welfare because the state will no longer allow him to work, but enough editorializing.

Because borrowing the money to build your own home is extremely difficult, for the purpose of this discussion, we will assume that you are either going to build this house with money you have saved, materials you have accumulated, or both. Even experienced licensed contractors face a real challenge getting construction loans, and usually the only way an owner-builder can get financing is by working with a contractor recognized by the bank and then following a strict performance schedule.

By a wide margin, the most comfortable way (unless you have an uncommon relationship with a banker) to build your own home is to have the resources in advance, pay as you build, or secure private financing until the house is finished and therefor financeable.

Site Preparation

Now that you're ready, where do you start?

The nuts and bolts instructions for building a house are published in many forms. The very best we have found for the construction of a wood-framed building is *A Graphic Guide to Frame Construction* by Rob Thallon (see Resource Guide). This book covers every detail from the very beginning of the project to the very end, and supports the clear and concise text with excellent drawings. The book is thoughtfully arranged and well indexed, making it a snap to find even the most obscure detail.

The first project will be site-preparation. If you will need a dozer to come in and level a building site, get several bids on the job, if at all possible, and referrals. There are operators who can wield a huge dozer with unbelievable finesse, and there are others who should be doing something else for a living.

We have come across operators who are sensitive to our desire to save the trees, and we've encountered those who treat trees with clear disdain. The difference in prices for heavy-equipment work from one operator to the next is often significant. Find the guy with the equipment suited to the task. If you need a small spot cleared out of a lovely forest, and the surrounding trees are important to you, find someone with a small dozer who is willing to discuss carefully avoiding damaging the trees you want to save.

There are good reasons to hire a smaller machine to do your dozing work. Price is one of them. In most cases, the operator will charge you, on top of his hourly rate, a "move-in" fee to cover his time and expenses in getting the machine to and from your job site. The bigger the machine, the bigger the equipment necessary to move it, hence the bigger the fee.

Another good reason for using smaller equipment is that a small dozer is much more maneuverable in a small space. If your site preparation involves working around trees or other natural terrain features that you would like preserved, maneuverability becomes important.

You'll also find guys who will try to convince you of the danger of having trees near your house: fire danger and the possibility of falling branches. That's your decision; not theirs. It's always been our choice to put up with the supposed risks in order to have the shade and ambiance provided by the trees.

Anyway, talk to the people from whom you get bids and find out how they feel about the things that are important to you. It is so much easier to work with someone who feels as you do about these issues than to have to argue constantly with your subcontractors to get the job done as you want it.

During site preparation is a good time to do any septic-tank, cesspool or sewer-access excavation, too. This can be left for later, but if one contractor does several jobs at the same time, it will usually cost you less. Another reason for getting the septic system out of the way is that the plumber (if you hire one) can hook up the sewer when he's ready to do it instead of having to make another trip later. And often, several excavation operations involve cleaning up the same mess several times.

If you are hooking up to a sewer system, try to schedule the actual connection so that the excavation contractor can back-fill the hole before he moves his equipment out. If you need any road-work done, see if he can't get that out of the way, too.

While the site is being cleared is a good time to get your electrical permit and put in a request for temporary power if you will be hooking up to the grid. Inquire about the options of underground or overhead lines to the building. Often, you can have your excavator put in the necessary ditch and it won't cost any extra to run the line underground. If you will be hiring an electrician, he will probably be the one who applies for the electrical permit and installs the "temporary." Contact him to schedule this work as soon as possible. The temporary should be in before the foundation work gets started.

The temporary consists of a post set into the ground and properly braced, with a breaker panel, several outlets, and an adequate ground. If you're doing your own wiring, the power company will tell you exactly what is required for the temporary hookup.

If you are building beyond the power lines and are going to install your own electrical system, consider a safely assembled, temporary hookup of your equipment before you start construction. If a photovoltaic array is to be part of the plan and is not going to be mounted on the house, having it installed prior to construction is a good idea. Otherwise, at least assemble your batteries, inverter, and backup generator in such a way that you don't need to run the generator all the time. Run the generator to power tools big enough to require its use, and have the batteries charging at the same time so that your small power tools can be run off the batteries through the inverter.

Regardless of how you set up your temporary power system, install it in an enclosure that will both allow plenty of ventilation and protect the equipment from the elements (and tampering, if applicable).

Subcontractors

If you're going to hire an electrician, be sure to talk over your alternative-power system before even asking for a bid. Some electricians welcome the challenge of something different and innovative; others want to stick with what they already know how to do. Find one who encourages the use of alternative power. Also, be sure to tell the building department right up front that you intend to install your own power system.

If you will be having phone service installed, see about having it run in early and having a phone on the job site. It doesn't take many trips to town to pay for a month's phone service.

Depending on what type of foundation you intend to use, you may also elect to subcontract this job to a pro. We have found that there is a small difference in price between subbing out foundations and doing them ourselves. The subcontractor has all of the materials and supplies that he will need for the concrete forms. The concrete subcontractor also gets concrete at a discount not available to the owner-builder. An excavation inspection is sometimes required before foundation forms go in, especially in areas of questionable soil integrity.

If you do the job yourself, you'll need a lot of plywood and other materials that, if you have to buy new, are expensive. And after using plywood for forms, it's a mess to use for anything else; it's hard to clean and never gets clean enough to avoid wiping out saw blades from imbedded cement and sand. If you still want to do your own foundations, plan your form material so that it can be re-used for subfloor in the building, and clean it as soon as the forms are stripped. A foundation inspection is usually required before the floor framing begins.

While your foundations are in progress, make an appointment with the plumber for his subfloor phase of the job. If you're doing the job yourself, get your materials list together and price the supplies you'll need. The subfloor plumbing goes in before the floor decking is installed. A subfloor inspection is usually required at this time, too.

The next appointment with the plumber will be when the house is completely framed and roofed. The plumbing should be finished before any wiring goes in because it's a whole lot easier to run wiring around plumbing than vice-versa. The roofing must be intact so that all through-the-roof vents can be properly sealed to the roofing material.

The next time your electrician will need to be called is when the house is completely framed, roofed, plumbed, and (preferably) weather tight. It's a good idea to clean up the building before the plumbers and electricians show up. They are much more efficient if they don't have to work around materials, saw-horses and debris. Also, many plumbers and most electricians leave an unbelievable mess in their wakes. Again, keep the work space cleaned up for efficiency, safety and morale.

Inspections

Before any insulation or interior wall surfaces get installed, three (or possibly four) inspectors will need to be called in. Electrical, plumbing, and rough-framing inspections are all in order now, as well as mechanical, if applicable. Some localities require mechanical permits and inspections for any installations of heating, cooling or exhaust-fan equipment and any associated duct-work. Fireplaces and wood stoves usually require permits and inspections, as well.

It's a good idea to make appointments with inspectors a little ahead of when you'll need them on the job site. Most will only be available on certain days of the week, and a little planning on your part will insure that your job won't be held up any longer than necessary waiting for inspections.

Your electrician will probably install at least a couple of working outlets in the house at the time he does the rough-in wiring, so that you will have the convenience of interior outlets for your power tools, and so that the temporary can be disconnected and the permanent hookup can be made to the grid or your alternate.

Passed all the inspections? There's one more before the drywall goes on: insulation, if required.

By the way, insulation is another of those jobs where it is often not much more expensive to have someone else install it than to buy it and install it yourself. Lots of folks experience a bad reaction to exposure to the dust created by the handling of fiberglass insulation. If you are one of them, get some bids. The installers are listed under "insulation-contractors" in the yellow pages.

Now you're ready for drywall, paneling, and finish work. The finish-work phase of building a house often takes as long as the whole project up to this point. This is particularly true in houses with a lot of attention to detail in moldings, staircases, cabinets and trim.

Remove all doors, window screens, and anything else you don't want to see paint on, before any texturing or spray-painting takes place. Do your masking very carefully, too. It is always faster and easier to take a little more time to do your masking and covering neatly and carefully than it is to remove the overspray later.

Make sure that there are no holes in the tarps and/or masking paper that covers tubs, shower enclosures and windows. Sprayed texture and paint manages to find its way into the most unlikely places. When masking around windows, be careful not to stretch the tape, especially in corners. When the tape gets damp from the texture compound or paint, it shrinks a little, and if it's even a little bit stretched, it will pull away from the surface it is supposed to protect--generally in those spots that are the most difficult to reach to clean up.

When all interior surfaces are finished (and painted, if applicable), and all the kitchen and bathroom floor-coverings and cabinets are in place, it's time for the electrician (or you) to install light fixtures, hook up appliances, etc. At about the same time (but not *at* the same time), the plumber will do his finish work: installing tub and shower hardware and faucets, hooking up disposal and dishwasher, and so on. (Make sure that any appliances you want the electrician and plumber to hook up are permanently in place before the workmen arrive on the job site.) Remember to call for appointments a little ahead of time, and schedule them so that no two contractors will be tripping over each other. Of course, all of this assumes that you are left with no alternative but to hire these things done.

The only inspections left are the electrical, plumbing, mechanical, and general finish inspections, and these are usually fairly casual walk-throughs.

When your inspections are done, you're basically on your own. Do consider building all of your own cabinets, too. You can set up a temporary cabinet shop in the just-weathertight house. If you don't have the necessary tools or skills, you can buy a good book on cabinet building and all of the tools and materials you'll need, and still come out way under what commercial cabinets will cost. And you'll have some nice tools for the next job. Any additional finish work, including re-hanging of doors and the installation of carpeting and any other floor-coverings, is about all that's keeping you from moving in to your new home.

GAS
S.C.

Alternative Electrical Systems

Testing Your Options

Most folks seem to feel that alternative electricity ought to be powered by the sun, wind, or water. If you are lucky enough to live in an area that will support any of these options, and if your power needs are either modest enough or your budget is big enough, sun, wind, and water are the ways to go.

Hydroelectric Generators

A hydroelectric system is ideal, because it runs day and night and its performance is not dependent on good weather. But there are two major considerations. The first, of course, is having access to a stream with sufficient volume and drop to make it work.

The suppliers of hydroelectric hardware can give you the methods and formulas necessary to determine the potential of a stream (see Resource Guide). But a second consideration, at times insurmountable, is dealing with bureaucracies.

We have heard some truly disheartening stories from folks with a perfect stream flowing right through their own land, and from which some echelon of government refuses to allow them to divert any water. Seems odd, that the big guys can use our river waters to cool their nuke plants, but us common folks aren't allowed to touch the "government's" water, period.

If you feel that hydroelectric will work for you, check the Resource Guide for specifics.

Solar Systems

The next best electrical system is solar, if you have enough year 'round sunshine to make it worthwhile. Solar panels and the necessary voltage-control hardware, while down in price from a few years ago, are still expensive. Depending upon whose guarantees you believe, the panels themselves also seem to have a finite life expectancy, so their replacement cost will have to be figured into your cost comparisons eventually. If you can get by with a modest amount of day-to-day power and then rely on a generator to fill in when you need more, a hybrid system is a good alternative.

Solar-driven electrical systems are ideal for homes with modest electrical requirements. This means that you will not be using electricity for cooking, room- or water-heating, or refrigeration. The exception to the refrigeration exclusion is one of the super-efficient (read: super-expensive, in the neighborhood of $2000) fridges, like a Sun Frost.

There are, of course lots of solar-powered homes that enjoy every electrical convenience imaginable, and except for prolonged sessions of bad weather, never need to turn on a generator. These homes are equipped with state-of-the-art systems that include large banks of batteries; extensive, automatic, sun-tracking solar-collector arrays; high-tech inverters; plus all of the sophisticated electrical hardware necessary to automate the system.

If you can afford the initial outlay required for a system that is designed from the outset to take care of all your electrical needs, certainly, go for it. Here on the Island of Hawai'i, there are many homes beyond the power lines. A lot of them run on the sun and need to use their backup generators only on occasion. The owners of several of these systems tell us that the initial cost of a system that will power an average three-bedroom home runs between five and ten thousand dollars.

The wide spread covers the differences between the systems which can range from barely adequate for supplying basic needs to fully capable of supplying everything but cooking, heating and refrigeration. Some systems are fully automatic, requiring expensive control hardware; others need more attention from the owners to keep everything in balance. Almost all of the solar homes here use propane for cooking and refrigeration.

There are several excellent books on solar electrical systems (see Resource Guide). They can guide you through the decisions for balancing your system between solar collectors and backup generator, and they can give you specific instructions on how to set up the system that will suit your needs.

If you live in an area where alternative electrical systems are fairly common, there will be businesses around that specialize in the sales, installation and maintenance of these systems. Based on your input, these folks can give you a quick estimate of the cost involved of setting up a complete system. That estimate will tell you right away whether or not such a system is within your budget.

Wind Generators

Wind generators come in all sizes, from little ones designed to keep the battery charged at a tiny mountain cabin, to units that will run an entire household with ease. The bigger the generator, the more wind required to drive it. The bigger generators are heavy and necessarily offer a lot of resistance to the wind, so their towers need to be substantial, adding to the cost of the initial installation.

Wind generators are fairly expensive to buy and install, and they need periodic maintenance. The maintenance means climbing to the top of a high-as-you-can-afford tower. Some of them are also quite noisy, so their placement needs special consideration.

There are some relatively new wind generators available now that can be mounted directly to a roof atop a short mast. They'd be worth looking into if your electrical demands are light.

Wind generators are at their best in areas of consistent, predictable, year-round wind. Installations near seacoasts need special attention because of the corrosive effects of salt air. Again, local suppliers can give you the necessary information to determine if your area has enough consistent wind to make it feasible. The Resource Guide lists specific publications that offer more information.

Fuel-powered Generators

And then there are fuel-powered generators. Because we had no usable stream, because the sun hid out for the four coldest months of the year, and because we had very little wind, we used fossil fuels to generate our electricity for ten years at our place in the mountains. We operated two businesses from our homestead and had to be able to depend on a consistent supply of clean, stable 110- volt power. Our particular operation included the use of a lot of power tools, a large air compressor, two computers, printers, a photocopier, plus the normal trappings of a sixteen-hundred square foot house.

Because we also operated the shop business from our home and needed more power than could be supplied by any kind of affordable solar system, we felt our generator was an ecologically-sound alternative. (See the next chapter to learn how we did it.)

The burning of fossil fuels to create electrical power may appear primitive or even obscene in the midst of technology which uses no non-renewable resources, but the actual application of that technology leaves a lot to be desired, at least to those of us on a budget. Looking through catalogs of photovoltaic hardware can be really inspiring until you get to the prices.

What if, as we did, you live in one of the many parts of our planet where the sun lurks behind clouds a good many months of the year? What if you live where the wind doesn't blow hard enough most of the year to operate a wind generator? And what if you don't have on your property a stream with sufficient drop to operate a viable hydroelectric system? Your only choice for self-sufficient power may be a generator. (The monthly fuel costs for operating the tiny, one-cylinder diesel generator in our well-designed and carefully managed system were less than some of our neighbors' costs for operating the *backup* generators for their solar/generator hybrid systems.)

Systems

A generator doesn't have to be obscene. A generator, as a matter of fact, can be a very efficient alternative energy source. The trick is to make it PART OF A SYSTEM instead of a SOLE SOURCE of power.

Regarding generators, there are several basic no-no's that when violated, do indeed make their use primitive and obscene. Here is a list of some of them:

1. NEVER operate a generator in such a way that your neighbors can hear it.

2. NEVER use a 3600 RPM gasoline-powered generator for anything but short-term applications such as emergencies or intermittent power tool use.

3. NEVER run a generator for any length of time for the sole purpose of operating equipment that requires far less power than the generator delivers. For example, don't spend the evening watching a 15-watt TV that's being powered by a 3500-watt generator. (Don't laugh. We had a neighbor who did just that almost every night of the week.)

The key to the efficient use of a generator for permanent homestead power is the STORAGE OF ELECTRICITY. Operate the generator ONLY when lots of power is required, as on the days of the week you do your laundry, vacuum the house, operate your shop, pump irrigation water or any other heavy use.

Then while the generator is running anyway, it can also operate an industrial-strength battery charger. The charger will charge the batteries that run the lighter loads of the house when the generator is not running. The low-voltage direct current supplied by the batteries is changed to regular 110 alternating current by an inverter. The key to the efficiency of this system is to have enough battery-storage capacity to run your house between the times you need the generator for heavy-duty use.

We ran our homestead on a system like this for ten years. Our home had all of the electrical gadgets found in any home in the city, plus an office, and a shop full of power tools. And we almost never ran the generator in the evening or on weekends.

Choosing a Generator

So how do you choose a generator? The cardinal rule of generator shopping is DO NOT EVEN CONSIDER A GASOLINE-POWERED UNIT THAT RUNS AT 3600 RPM, for several good reasons. Almost all of these machines are built for intermittent use only. Almost all of them will self-destruct quickly when used for prolonged periods at even modest loads. Almost all are optimistically over-rated.

For example, we borrowed a popular-brand Japanese generator to use while our good old industrial machine was down for its first repair in years of service. The old generator was rated at 3500 watts and would easily start any power tool in the shop even when the air-compressor was running. The borrowed unit, resplendent in chrome razzle-dazzle and complete with automotive-style operating panel (even an ignition key!) was rated at 5500 watts--but it would not even start the compressor. It just huffed and puffed, lugged down, and popped its circuit-breaker.

Another reason to avoid the gas-powered generators is noise. 3600 RPM gasoline generators, running under load, are incredibly noisy. Someone called us to ask if we had ever heard one of the new Honda generators run. He said that the dealer fired one up inside the showroom and it fairly whispered. But what the dealer DID NOT do was plug something into the machine which would have brought it up to its normal operating speed. Many of the bigger high-speed gas generators have an idle feature which allows the engine to slow way down when there is no load on the generator. Then the instant the generator senses a load, the machine comes up to its full-scream speed. Buyer beware.

Enough of the DON'Ts. Let's take a look at some DOs.

A "generator" is actually composed of two major components: the generator (or alternator, depending on the machine), which produces the electricity, and the engine, which drives the generator. It is important that each of these major components is carefully selected to do its required job.

Generators that are serious contenders for permanent installation will operate at a maximum speed of 1800 RPM. (Be careful not to confuse "running" speed with "idle" speed. Some of the generators that have an idle speed of 1800 RPM run at 3600 RPM.)

One of the best industrial-quality (1800 RPM) gasoline-powered generators available has the bonus of also being an electric welder. A good-quality arc welder can be a real asset on the homestead. Even if you don't know the first thing about welding, having the machine available makes it easy for someone who does know how to use it to do any repairs that require welding.

Check your yellow pages for a welding-supplies dealer who handles Miller products and ask to see the lineup of welder-generators. They come in various outputs and all have excellent engines designed for continuous operation at full-rated output. These machines run at 1800 RPM in "generator" mode and at 3600 RPM in "welder" mode.

The machine which ran our home and shop first was a Miller welder/generator. Its engine just loafed along, producing its full-rated power and the only problems we ever had with the Kohler engine on our Miller generator were a few minor repairs.

RV Generators

Another source for industrial-quality, low-speed generators is your nearest dealer in RV supplies. Any generator with the name Kohler or Onan can be counted on for a long and trouble-free life. Be careful though to make sure that you are getting an 1800 RPM machine. Some of the smaller units run at 3600 RPM.

If you do get an RV generator, do not remove any of the sheet-metal shrouding. These machines are designed to be installed in the small spaces available in RVs and the shrouding is necessary to insure the proper flow of cooling air. This specialized shrouding can be replaced with the standard shroud supplied with an engine designed to run in an open environment, but it is essential that the correct flow of cooling air be directed over and through the finned cylinder-head.

Onan and/or Kohler generators are also available as free-standing machines and these are actually better suited to permanent installation.

However, the most efficient and maintenance-free engines of all are diesels. Diesels have no ignition system, carburetor, nor spark plugs. Diesels are simple in design and extremely durable. They burn LOTS less fuel per horsepower/hour than do gasoline engines, and their exhaust is devoid of many of the toxic emissions of gas engines.

The catch is that it is difficult to find diesel-powered generators in the small sizes required by the average homestead. Kubota and Yanmar have recently introduced several versions of small diesel generators. The engines in these units run at speeds up to 3600 RPM, and the life expectancy of the engine, according to the service personnel we've talked to, seems to vary from 2000 to 10,000 hours. 10,000 hours isn't too bad, but anything like 2000 hours before the engine needs an overhaul is unacceptable.

The one real virtue of these machines is that they are fairly quiet. The Kubota units have liquid-cooled engines and are certainly worth investigating, particularly for a system that needs its generator primarily for backup use. When selecting your generator, remember that it is *not* efficient to operate a generator which produces, or is capable of producing, a lot more power than is required. See the Resource Guide for more information on these machines.

Neighborhood Hook-ups

One application of a larger diesel generator that might work well in some circumstances is an installation which would serve several neighbors. Each neighbor's house would have its own battery bank and inverter. The generator would come on line for a predetermined duration each day, supplying each home with large amounts of power AND charging the batteries to carry the load for the balance of the day. The cost of the machine and the maintenance chores would be shared by the neighbors.

The 8KW to 25KW generators driven by small diesel engines made in China (See Resource Guide) are excellent alternative-system power sources. These little engines burn only 1/2 pint of fuel per horsepower/hour, and the generators supplied with them are state-of-the-art. It is not uncommon for these engines to run for 50,000 hours before needing any major attention. And the generators come with an overhaul kit and the tools to do it with. (See the next chapter.)

Phantom Loads and Inverters

There is much talk in alternative-energy circles of "phantom loads." Phantom loads are those loads on your electrical system which accomplish little but are always there, such as clocks in appliances, "automatic-on" circuits in remote-start electronics, timers, and inverters which are left on 24 hours a day.

When calculating your power needs, don't overlook phantom loads in gadgets like calculators, battery chargers, answering machines, etc., that have little adapters/transformers which are always plugged into the wall. These adapters are constantly drawing power, even if the gadget they supply is turned off. If you have several even seemingly-insignificant phantom loads, they can add up to a debilitating drain on your system unless it is designed to accommodate them.

The high-end inverters which we recommend (like the Trace, Heliotrope and Heart units) draw about a half a watt at idle. As a comparison, a 25-watt light bulb left on for thirty minutes uses about the same amount of power as one of these inverters uses in 24 hours of standby service. You will have to decide whether leaving your inverter on all the time is feasible in your particular electrical system.

Finally...

In summary, a generator used as either a sole source of power or as a backup for other sources does not need to be an environmental disaster. The generator should be operated in a controlled and orderly fashion, and only when required for high-load applications. Surplus power should be diverted into storage batteries for use when the generator is not on-line. A system like this can supply a home with uninterrupted 110-volt power 24 hours a day even if the generator is not started for several days at a time.

Stay away from "consumer" generators, regardless of buzz-words like "heavy-duty." The generators on most of the 3600 RPM machines available through hardware outlets are fine for their intended uses: occasional power tools, pumps, and emergencies. Most will fail quickly if subjected to sustained operation at anywhere near their maximum output, let alone their optimistically-rated output. The engines on these machines are well-suited to their intended use, which is intermittent operation.

Almost any generator designed to operate at 1800 RPM is also designed to run quietly and dependably for years while producing its rated output. Commercial/industrial equipment is the best way to go. If you live on a homestead or farm and for some reason do not want to install a diesel generator, do consider the welder/generator combination.

Again, be careful. There are welder/generators on the market that run at 3600 RPM. And though they are designed for industrial use, they will not last as long as their slower-running cousins. They are also noisier. And you will have to endure the excessive noise for the duration, even if it is shorter than you'd hoped.

Diesel engines outlast gasoline engines by a wide margin, burn considerably less fuel, and require no maintenance other than regular oil and filter changes.

If you happen to come across a good, used, military-surplus or other industrial-type machine, and you are not intimate with the electrical workings of generators, have someone knowledgeable check it over for you. Older generators will often have very complex and possibly malfunctioning voltage-regulating hardware that can cost more to straighten out than the machine is worth. And remember, don't buy a generator that is capable of producing way more power than you need.

As with all mechanical equipment, follow the manufacturer's service recommendations. The importance of timely oil changes cannot be overstressed. You can save money on oil, but not by buying Brand-X. Buy your major-name-brand product of the proper viscosity in case lots when it comes on sale.

With diesel engines, use only oil that is specifically rated for diesel use. (It will say so on the container.) Diesel engines operate at much higher combustion pressures than gasoline engines and regular automotive motor oil is not suitable.

Never operate your generator without a properly installed and serviced air cleaner. It doesn't take much abrasive dust to dramatically shorten the life of an engine.

Install your generator in a clean, well-ventilated shed, out of the weather and out of the paths of dust and moisture.

Be sure that your generator has come up to full speed before applying any load. Starting a generator with an electrical load on it is hard on both the generator and the equipment plugged into it. It is also good practice to allow the machine to run at no load for a few minutes before shutting it down, especially after it has been working hard.

With intelligent and conservative use, a well-chosen and properly maintained generator can become the heart of a dependable and cost-effective alternative energy system.

In any event, your electrical system is going to be with you for a long time. It deserves to be thoroughly researched, thoughtfully designed, and carefully constructed. It should be built with dependability and permanence as the primary focus. Plan your electrical needs, not only for right now, but for the foreseeable future as well. It's a lot cheaper to build your system with the future in mind than to upgrade it later. Buying cheap components not intended for full-time use may save you a little at the outset, but you'll pay more than the difference when you have to replace them.

All this talk of generators might make you think that we are trying to talk you out of utilizing solar power. Not at all! By all means, research your needs and balance your system in favor of solar if at all possible. In many cases adding as many solar panels as you can afford to a hybrid system will mean less run-time for the generator. However, if you will be needing substantial amounts of power for several hours a day (as for a shop), the stored surplus power from your generator just might be all that's required to run your house for the rest of the day.

We will always do our best to discourage anyone from planning a 12-volt electrical system for any purpose other than a small cabin. Twelve-volt tools and appliances are almost all specifically designed for use in recreational vehicles, on an occasional and light-duty basis. They don't hold up well under day-to-day household use. They're more expensive than the much sturdier 110-volt models. They are more difficult to get serviced and to find parts for. And, while there is a vast variety of 110-volt tools and small appliances, the selection from the 12-volt lineup is extremely limited.

Since most alternative electrical systems use batteries, it used to be practical to use 12-volt lighting for at least the overall basic lighting system in the house. Because the power (12 volts) would be drawn directly from the batteries, there was no need to have an inverter on all the time just to run lights. We still recommend that at least some of the permanent lighting in the house be supplied directly from the batteries.

But in most cases, modern inverters and today's 110-volt PL lighting are so efficient that they can be used effectively for most lighting needs. The only exception to this practice would be a system that barely supplies enough power to meet the system's demands. Then it becomes important to conserve everything possible, even to turning off an inverter that draws less than one watt at standby.

The only time we ever turned off our inverter was when we left home for several days at a time. More on these inverters later.

Our Electrical System

How It Came to Be

'Way back in 1979, we decided to move to a beautiful 108 acres of forest we had bought in North-Central Oregon. There were no buildings on the property; we were going to start from scratch. The nearest power line was a little more than a half-mile down the road, and even before the utility company quoted us $10,000 to run in the power, we had pretty much made up our minds that we wanted to generate our own electricity.

We spent the year before our move making plans, gathering information and supplies. Part of "gathering information" included visiting the other folks who were already doing what we wanted to do: start with bare land and build a homestead, do it all on our own, and remain as independent as possible. We paid a lot of attention to how these folks were dealing with their lack of store-bought electricity.

Most of them handled it in a way which was, to us, unacceptable. They often relied on smelly, dangerous kerosene lamps for most of their lighting. They used small, gasoline-powered generators to run what few electrical gadgets they felt necessary, they had a bare minimum of electric lighting in their homes, and what lights they did have were often automotive light bulbs mounted in aluminum pie-plate reflectors! Some went a step further and used car batteries to keep a couple of little lights and maybe a car radio running when the generator wasn't out there wailing away.

We remember one couple sitting around for hours in the evenings watching their 12" black-and-white TV. Their 3500-watt Sears generator was in the yard screaming its heart out to run a 15-watt TV! (We could hear their generator from our place 3/4 mile away.) We never did convince them that those machines were not designed to be run for hours on end, but Sears was really great about honoring their warranty and replacing their generators as they blew up.

Of all the people we visited, nobody had what we considered an acceptable alternative electrical system. We listened to endless hours of dialogue on solar panels, twelve-volt appliances, and all of the vague theories which came from the many books on the subject of building one's own power system. And we read all the books ourselves.

Selecting a System

Almost all of these systems had a common shortfall: their inability to run off-the-shelf 110-volt tools, appliances, office equipment, and music systems. Not only did we want our system to be able to handle these things, we wanted them 24 hours a day. And we didn't want to have to have a generator running all the time to pull it off. We knew exactly what we wanted our system to do.

For although we were going to be living in our owner-built home in the woods sixteen miles from the nearest town, we did not plan to do without what we considered life's pleasures. These included a high-quality music system, a washer and dryer, microwave and other small kitchen appliances, and a lot of office equipment which would later include two computers, printers, a full-function copier and a fax machine. We were also going to be building a shop near the house, and in this shop we would earn our keep, using all sorts of power-tools ranging from table-saws and jointers to a commercial air compressor.

There are those who say that because of our toys, we blaspheme to call ourselves homesteaders. Some claim that homesteaders should live lives of denial to prove their worth. We think not. It is important to us to be able to go into the kitchen at ten o'clock at night and heat a snack in the microwave; to be able to have the VCR automatically start recording a favorite movie at midnight. And we like to feel that if we can have all of these comforts and provide them with our own ingenuity, that we still qualify as real homesteaders.

We knew in advance that a 3600-RPM, portable generator was not going to do the job. None of them is designed for any kind of continuous-duty service; and even if one were, the noise level is completely unacceptable, the fuel consumption unbelievable, and the maintenance requirements are a nuisance at best. We also knew that we would not be satisfied with having to trudge outside to start and stop a generator whenever we needed some power, particularly in the middle of winter.

Matter of fact, we knew that we wouldn't be satisfied having to start a generator every time we needed some power, even if we could do it with a wish!

Knowing what the electrical system was going to run made it possible to set its parameters. It had to deliver at least six kilowatts of clean, stable 110 and 220-volt electricity during those times when the shop was in operation. It had to be able to deliver at least 1200 watts of clean, stable

110-volt power 24 hours a day. It had to be fully automatic and remote-controlled, so that we would never have to leave the house or the shop to start or stop a generator. It had to be quiet enough so that we could not hear it from the house. It had to be nearly maintenance-free, and it had to do all of this for an operating expense of $25 per month. We had an initial-outlay budget of $4000.

Meeting Demands

Well, we did it. And in doing so, we proved that just because we lived beyond the power lines, we didn't have to do without any of the luxuries which only clean, steady, dependable 110-volt power can provide. And we did it with standard, low-tech hardware, in a way which could be duplicated by anyone who doesn't want to deal with the perpetual nuisances of fragile, thirsty, noisy generators; outfitting a home with fragile, overpriced and hard to find (and get fixed) 12-volt tools, appliances, radios, and the like; or even living with the limited amount of electricity provided by a solar-powered system we could have built for the same investment. (No solar-powered system that could be built for the same money would have been able to operate the shop on its own, so a generator would have been necessary anyhow.)

Ours was the ideal system for the family with a home business requiring the use of power tools. Our system powered our home and shop for ten years without a hitch. The system had evolved to the point where it dependably ran our place--home and shop--for about $25 a month total cost. During the winter storms, our TV news programs informed us that our rural electric service was down because of tree limbs falling on ice-covered lines. We didn't have a single blackout in ten years!

The basics of the system were simple: a generator, a bank of storage batteries, an inverter to change the stored power into usable 110-volt electricity, and a charger to keep the batteries charged.

So why was this particular system so special? During ten years of use, it evolved into the ideal combination of components; a balance was achieved which allowed each part of the system to work at its best potential.

When we started out, we were using a Miller "Roughneck" industrial quality combination generator/welder for our main power source. This very dependable, gasoline-powered machine was permanently installed in a shed near the shop, and wired to be remote-controlled from either the house or the shop. The Miller generator runs at only 1800 RPM, so is fairly quiet and for our electrical demands the first few years, it worked pretty well. The Miller is an industrial machine designed to put out its full-rated 3500 watts continuously. It did, and then some.

Even in the early years our electrical system was designed to get the most efficient use out of each component, and that meant that the generator was rarely turned on unless it was going to be cranking out nearly all it could. Our household could run for several days off the batteries, and the generator was never turned on unless it had several hours work waiting for it. While it did that work, it also recharged the batteries.

The Miller served us well for about five-thousand hours--an amazing feat for a little gas engine. (We take very good care of our equipment.) During that time it used about a gallon of fuel for each three hours of running and it went through several sets of points, a magneto, two carburetor rebuilds, and two fuel pumps. It was still running well when we replaced it with the generator set which put us in the serious power-producing business.

The new generator had to meet a new set of standards: it had to produce at least six kilowatts; it had to have a state-of-the-art, fully voltage-regulated, brushless alternator; and it had to be driven by a diesel engine.

Gas to Diesel

Why diesel? Diesel engines are wonderful. They have no spark plugs, carburetors or ignition systems. They need no tune-ups. They are unbelievably dependable. They produce their amazing amounts of torque at very low RPM so they last almost forever. They use less than half the amount of fuel per horsepower/hour than do gas engines. And diesel fuel doesn't pollute the air with lead. They are also very expensive.

We called every supplier of commercial diesel generator sets we could find, and were quoted prices from several thousand dollars for a "good used set" to figures that made us start thinking in terms of gas engines again. Then we remembered an ad we had seen about diesel engines made in, of all places, mainland China. We called the advertiser and had him send us his literature.

The claims he made seemed too good to believe, so we called back and asked if they had ever sold one of their machines to anyone living within a day's drive of our place. We wanted to see one in action, and talk to its owner.

They gave us three names, addresses and phone numbers of owners of their equipment, all within an hour's drive of us. Needless to say, we immediately called the closest one and set up an appointment for the same day.

His machine was installed close enough to his house that he didn't think it an inconvenience to go outside to start it. He also thought it was so much fun to start it by hand, that he never bothered to hook up the electric starter that came with it. While we watched, he walked over to the pretty little engine, inserted the crank, pulled open the compression-release lever, cranked the engine over twice, released the compression-release--and it was running! No glow-plugs (as in many diesels), no starting fluid; just a hand crank. We were impressed.

With the engine putt-putting along at a leisurely 1500 RPM, he put a good-sized load on the alternator, and there was no discernible change in engine speed or noise. The owner of this little gem was very pleased with it and especially pleased with the folks he bought it from.

We could hardly wait to get to the phone to order ours.

Right after we got off the phone, we started building our new generator shed. About a week later, the generator was installed and running. We installed a 275-gallon fuel tank right next to the shed that gravity-fed the fuel to the engine.

Thermo-syphon Cooling and Exhausting Options

Our cooling system consisted of a 55-gallon drum (of a mix of anti-freeze and water) installed at the proper height to create a thermo-syphoning coolant-circulation loop. This cooling system worked well in any kind of weather, and ours ranged from twenty below zero to the high nineties.

In cold weather, the thermo-syphoning cooling system really has an advantage over a more conventional radiator-type system. While the engine is running, the hot coolant from the engine enters the top of the tank. As it cools, it drops to the bottom of the tank and circulates back into the inlet port at the bottom of the engine. When the engine is shut down, the thermo-syphon effect comes to a stop, and eventually reverses. Now the warmer coolant at the top of the tank flows down through the engine and back into the tank to get re-warmed. The net effect of this is that after being shut down for 12-16 hours over a thirty-degree night, the engine will still be warm. It's a lot easier on the engine to start it warm than at thirty degrees.

We initially routed the exhaust through another 55-gallon drum buried in the ground behind the shed, as recommended by the engine supplier. But the drum-in-the-ground muffler created a little too much back-pressure, which helped carbon deposits form around the exhaust valve. That back pressure was responsible for the only service-interruption we ever experienced from our diesel engine. Eventually, the valve wouldn't close tightly enough to form a perfect seal. The engine still ran just fine, but it became difficult to start.

By "difficult" we mean that instead of starting instantly, it had to be cranked for a few seconds. We like to keep our equipment running smoothly, and the harder starting was a clear indication of a problem that would only get worse if left alone.

Using the manual and tools supplied with the generator, we removed the cylinder head, cleaned the combustion-chamber, reseated the valve and reassembled the engine. We discontinued the drum-in-the-ground muffler, going instead to a simple, straight pipe about fifteen feet tall. Good as new, and never another problem. We were back on line before the system batteries needed recharging.

The China Diesel Unit

The generator came with an electric starter, and it started so easily that wiring it for remote control from the house and the shop was a breeze. Since we couldn't hear the engine from the house, we installed an intercom between the shed and the house. To start the generator from the house, we first turned on the intercom, started the engine, and turned off the intercom. Sometimes we turned on the intercom for a moment or two just to enjoy hearing that faithful little engine doing its thing.

The engine was indeed made in China. It was a fifty-year old design, so it was the very essence of simplicity. The only thing which deviated from the original design was the metallurgy and the design and materials of bearings and seals.

We have talked to several people who have run these amazing little engines for thousands of hours, including a mechanic who services them, and the reports all came back positive. The mechanic had just torn down one with fifty-thousand hours on it, and the bearings and cylinder walls were like new.

By the way, fifty-thousand hours figures out to eight hours a day, seven days a week, for *seventeen years*. And the engine comes with all of the parts and tools to do an overhaul. As supplied from China Diesel Imports in Jamul California, the generator set comes with just the state-of-the-art alternator we were looking for, and is set up to produce 8000 watts. Since we didn't need that much power, we ordered ours with the correct drive pulley to produce 6000 watts.

CDI also sells several other configurations of generator sets, ranging from 8 to 25KW. When the 8KW machine is ordered for 6000 watt output, the machine comes with both pulleys, so it can be changed back to the higher output at any time. The benefit of the lower output is that the engine runs even more slowly than it does at the higher-output setting, saving fuel and wear.

Where We Started

Our first batteries were two deep-cycle 6-volt, 260-amp-hour, golf cart batteries, giving us 12 volts at 260 amp-hours. We chose these because of their low initial cost and high output. Using deep-cycle batteries is, of course, essential. The 12-volt batteries used in RVs don't have the capacity to run a house, and although there are better batteries on the market than the ones we were using, they are also very spendy. At that time, our house was small and the electric demands were fewer.

After five years, our house had doubled in size and we had added a lot more lights and electrical loads, so we put in a bigger battery-bank. The first set of batteries was still functioning, although not as they did when new.

During the summer, the batteries would carry the house for at least two days, and sometimes as long as a week. During winter, with its shorter days and more time spent indoors, we could get by for two days if we were frugal, but usually had to run the generator for a while nearly every day.

Things changed after installing the diesel. At five hours per gallon of diesel fuel, we just started it in the morning when we went out to the shop, and turned it off in the early afternoon. During an especially cold winter, (15 below zero!) we let it run 24 hours a day. This way, we wouldn't have to start the poor thing when it was that cold, and we could also keep electric heaters running in the tank- and poultry-houses and other strategic places.

With the new schedule of running the generator almost every day (easily justified by earning our living in the shop), low batteries became a thing of the past, and it is on this schedule that we computed our cost-of-operation at $25/month. And that included all operating costs, not just fuel.

These figures were based on late 1980's prices. The only price that has risen materially since then is that of fuel. Since fuel expense is only a part of the overall operating costs, the total figures would not be significantly higher at today's prices. We were also running a full-time shop when we figured the costs.

Inverters

Our inverter was a Heart Interface 1200-watt unit with a built-in battery charger. It worked like this: when the generator was running, the inverter worked as a high-power, fully automatic battery charger which shunted the generator's 110 directly into the house. It delivered the right amount of charge depending on the condition of the batteries. Once they reached a fully-charged state, it switched to a maintenance charge.

The instant that the inverter sensed that the generator turned off, it switched itself into inverter mode, supplying 110-volt power to the house from the batteries, without interruption. When the generator came on line again, the clever inverter jumped back into charger mode.

State-of-the-art high-efficiency inverters like the one we used are nothing like the small units sold for use in RVs. The small inverters are notoriously inefficient. The Heart, Trace, and other comparable units are not.

High-efficiency inverters draw less than one watt at idle, so they can be left them on line 24 hours a day. Ours ran the TV, VCR, stereo system, microwave, vacuum cleaner, sewing machine and our two computers and the rest of the office. It *is* necessary to pay attention to the total load, however.

Our particular inverter was rated at 1200 watts, so we couldn't turn on everything in the house at the same time when the generator wasn't running. The only things in our house which used enough power to really have to watch were the microwave and the toaster. The kitchen was wired in such a way that if these two appliances are turned on at the same time, a breaker tripped before any overload could damage the inverter. According to the manufacturers, these inverters can take an amazing instantaneous overload without damage; but it's pretty easy to avoid having to find out just how much.

Leaving an inverter on-line 24 hours a day may seem extravagant, but it really isn't, at least with this particular system. The only time we ever turned off our inverter was when we left home for several days at a time. A state-of-the-art inverter draws less power in a 24-hour day than does a 25-watt light bulb left on for one hour. It was worth it to us to have the convenience of full-time 110. Leaving it on full time meant that we could enjoy such luxuries as off-the-shelf, plug-in clock radios, a deluxe model microwave with a clock and timer, a VCR to automatically record movies when were not at home, and the convenience of operating anything in the house at any time we wished.

If we were in a house using solar collectors as its primary power source, we would install an extra panel to support the idle-power draw of the inverter for the convenience of full-time 110 power. Really, what if someone needed to send us an important fax in the middle of the night?

To Do It Again

We do not consider our level of electricity-use to be a luxury. When we have to produce enough power to operate the shop in which we earn our living, the house and office run basically for free. A definition of "for free": When the generator is producing enough power to operate the shop, the additional fuel required to supply the house and battery charger is an insignificant percentage of the total fuel-burn, which is usually around five hours running-time per gallon of diesel.

And at about $4000, our system was certainly not hi-tech, but neither was it primitive. It was simple, basic, extremely dependable, low maintenance; and it did everything we wanted it to.

We often had people suggest that we add some solar panels so we wouldn't have to run the generator so much. Any comparably priced photovoltaic installation would not have been able to supply enough electricity over its projected life span even to come close to paying for itself in our application.

In a household that didn't include a shop for which the generator must be run for a few hours every day, photovoltaics would indeed be a viable option. In our application, we needed a certain amount of power to operate that shop, and all of the power we used during the rest of the day is produced and stored at the same time the shop is in operation. Any addition of solar panels would only have succeeded in complicating a simple system and adding more maintenance hassles in the process. Besides, where we lived on our mountaintop, we rarely saw the sun between November and March, and those were really the times when the most power was required.

We no longer live with that system. In our quest to get closer to the ocean, we sold our homestead of ten years and moved to a little village on the Oregon coast. We moved into a small house that was to be our home until we found the perfect spot near the ocean where we were going to start all over again.

Well, those were our best-laid plans... We lived on the Oregon coast for about four years while diligently working toward owning our home free and clear. During that time, our community was "discovered," property values tripled, and there wasn't a block in town that didn't have at least one house under construction. Clearly, it was time to move on again, and we moved to Hawai'i.

As of this writing, we just need to find the right parcel of land, and we'll start all over again. Because we will have sunshine year 'round and not be as dependent on full-time shop use, we'll base the system on solar panels and use another Chinese diesel gen-set as our backup. Other than that, the system will be the same.

Water Systems on Alternative Power

What We Mean

This chapter deals with water systems for homes that do not have municipal water available and are operating their own independent electrical systems. This includes homes that are supplied with water from a well, spring, stream, rainwater catchment, pond, cistern, or any combination.

Throughout this book, we strive to avoid getting very specific with the nuts-and-bolts stuff; we guide you through your options and then direct you to specific reading in the Resource Guide. This chapter has had to be more specific because we could not find any material already available that covered all of the options available in this area.

Designing a water system for a conventional home on public power and with a normal water supply is easy and straightforward; if you don't already know how to do it, there are lots of books available to guide you (see the Resource Guide). Water systems for homes on alternative power are a different story. There are also some specialized cases where homes which are hooked to the grid still have to deal with unique water management problems, and the material in this chapter may apply to them, too.

In most cases, the plumbing in the house itself will be the same as in a conventional system. The differences are in the equipment required to get the water under pressure and then into the house. Again, check the Resource Guide for books to steer you through the basics of standard, residential plumbing. Some surprisingly good ones are also available at larger hardware stores and lumber yards.

IMPORTANT NOTE:

There are few places left on this planet where some bureaucracy hasn't established itself to tell you how you may or may not run your life. This is very apparent in all phases of home building, and especially so in the areas of plumbing and electrical systems. Before you even begin any specific design of your water system, be sure to contact the applicable bureaucracy. You need to tell them exactly what your intentions are; where your water source is and how you intend to utilize it. Don't just get a plumbing permit and assume that what you want to do is legal.

Every particular area has its own plumbing code idiosyncrasies, too. For example, there may be a uniform state-wide plumbing code, but your local inspectors might have their own preferences as to how a job gets done. Even if you are familiar with plumbing procedures, ask about the local rules before you begin. If possible, get into a home under construction and look over the plumbing. Check for any techniques that are unfamiliar to you. A good way to invite unreasonable scrutiny by your friendly plumbing inspector is to make it obvious by your unfamiliar techniques that you are a "foreigner."

In some places in this free country of ours, an individual is not allowed to plumb his or her own house! In this case, even if you are a retired plumbing contractor, you cannot plumb your own house without buying a new license. If you find yourself in this unfortunate position and must hire a licensed plumber, be sure to find one who is comfortable working with non-standard equipment and systems. Talk to your prospective plumber first. If he tells you right up front what a drag it is to do something out of the ordinary, find another plumber.

There are plumbers who will work with an owner-builder, although what they are doing stretches the rules a bit in some cases. Ask around; you will probably get some referrals to a plumber who will let you do at least some of the work, thereby reducing the amount of labor you will have to pay for.

Design Variables

There are about as many variables in the design requirements of wilderness-home water systems as there are homes to design them for. Some of them are:

Where the water comes from:
  Well, cistern, spring, creek, hauled-in.
  (A cistern can be supplied with water from a rain catchment system, or it can be hauled in or pumped in from a nearby creek or other source.)

The quantity of water available:
  High- or low-production well or spring, rationed trucked-in supply, seasonal supply, unlimited supply.

The quantity required:
  Limited residential use, small garden use, field irrigating, etc.

How it is stored:
  Pressure tank, gravity-feed (elevated) tank, ground-level tank, cistern.

What kind of electricity is available:
  220 volts AC, full-time 110, part-time 110, full- or part-time 12-volt DC. (Not as confusing as it sounds.)

The amount of that electricity that's available:
  How many amp-hours per day.

Let's discuss each of these variables briefly, and then apply them into viable combinations.

Where Does the Water Come From?

DEEP WELL: A deep well which requires a multi-horsepower submersible pump will also require a several-kilowatt power-source. These pumps can be made to work well on even a part-time electrical system, but they do require ample power to run them.

SHALLOW WELL: A fractional-horsepower jet-pump will usually do the job on a shallow well, and a jet pump will run with power supplied by either a part-time electrical system or a heavy-duty inverter, making 24-hour-a-day pump operation possible with part-time power.

SPRING: Pumping water from a spring can be done in several ways. Gravity-feed to a storage tank is ideal, but assumes that the tank can be placed below the level of the spring. When this isn't feasible, a pump must be used. The size of the pump depends entirely on the amount of water which must be moved.

CREEK: Since the location of the creek determines whether or not the water can be taken out above the level of the house, the requirements for pumps are the same as for springs.

RAINWATER CATCHMENT: Rainwater collected on a potable-water-safe roof and diverted through a system of gutters and piping into a catchment. The catchment can be any kind of tank large enough to supply the system through anticipated dry spells. Different types of catchments include above-ground tanks similar to swimming pools but with potable-water linings, concrete tanks (cisterns) both above-ground and below grade, fiberglass tanks, and others.

HAULED WATER: Water trucked in from a nearby spring, cistern, creek or other source too far away to pipe in directly. Some areas of the country have water-hauling services. They'll deliver the water to your place and pump it into your tank for a set fee, usually charged per thousand gallons. If this service isn't available, you can easily haul your own water. (We hauled our water for ten years; more on that, later.)

There are several ways to get hauled-in water to its points of use. You can pump the water directly from the tank-truck to your storage tank(s), either elevated or at ground level. Or if you're lucky enough to have a truck access point above the level of your tank, the water can be drained from the truck into the tank.

Pure, clean water

It should be noted here that this discussion does not delve into the safety of using surface water. You must use your own discretion when selecting water sources, and if the water is to be used for domestic purposes, it should always be tested by a competent lab.

"Planning for an Individual Water System" (see resource guide) covers, in great detail, all areas of testing water and ways to determine what is needed to provide a safe supply.

How Much Water Is Available?

If you have a well or spring which will out-produce your needs, you are indeed fortunate. Your storage facilities will generally not need to be very big, and possibly none will be needed at all.

If your daylight-hours demand is greater than your daylight-hours supply of water, but your 24-hour supply is enough to meet that daylight demand, you will need a storage facility large enough to contain the 24-hour supply. You simply fill the tank twenty-four hours a day, thus keeping ahead of the loss incurred mostly in the daytime.

If you are lucky enough to have a spring on a hillside thirty feet higher than your house, you need only to run a pipe to the house. No storage, no pumps, instant pressure!

How Much Water Do You Need?

The number of gallons-per-hour or gallons-per-day your household uses will be a major factor in deciding what type of pump you will need to supply it.

Food for thought

There are "normally accepted" statistics which show that the average American household uses 700 gallons of water per person, per day. For a family of three, that comes to about 63,000 gallons per month. This author's family of three lived with a comfortable and dependable water system using hauled-in water for about ten years. Total consumption rarely exceeded 1200 gallons per month. The house had all of the usual water-using conveniences: flush toilet, tub with shower, full kitchen, and laundry We even washed our car occasionally. This level of frugality requires nothing more than the willing co-operation of all of the family members.

You can do a rough guesstimate of how much water your family needs by counting up the weekly loads of laundry, approximate toilet flushes, loads of dishes, number of baths and/or showers, etc., and dividing by seven for the daily number. If you will be irrigating a garden, you'll just have to guess on that one. Five gallons per minute of watering is a good basis to work from.

If you are still living with metered water, check your water bill for the amount you're now using. Unless you will live a very different lifestyle in your new environs, don't count on using a lot less water than you're now using.

We had a very productive garden that we watered with trucked-in water, in serious dry-country. The secret to keeping the amount of water needed reasonable was planting in trenched rows and mulching. We dug nice, straight trenches for everything we planted, and mulched heavily with spoiled straw, free from neighboring ranchers. (Leaves would work, too.) We watered by carefully flooding each row about every three days. Mulch keeps moisture in: between the rows was dry as dust, and the veggies were thriving.

Here's an experiment for you: If you anticipate that you will have to get along on a minimum of water, try doing just that where you are now. Do your best for a month or two and then check your water bill to see just how much you really conserved. (If your water bill is expressed in cubic feet of water, multiply by 7.48 for the number of gallons you used.)

Water Conservation

We had a very productive garden that we kept watered with trucked-in water. And this was in some serious dry-country. The secret to keeping the amount of water needed down to a reasonable amount was planting in trenched rows and mulching. We dug nice, straight trenches for everything we planted, and mulched heavily with spoiled straw we got free from neighboring ranchers. (Leaves would work, too.)

Watering was done by carefully flooding each row about every three days. It is just amazing how that mulch keeps the moisture in! The ground between the rows would be dry as dust, and the veggies were thriving.

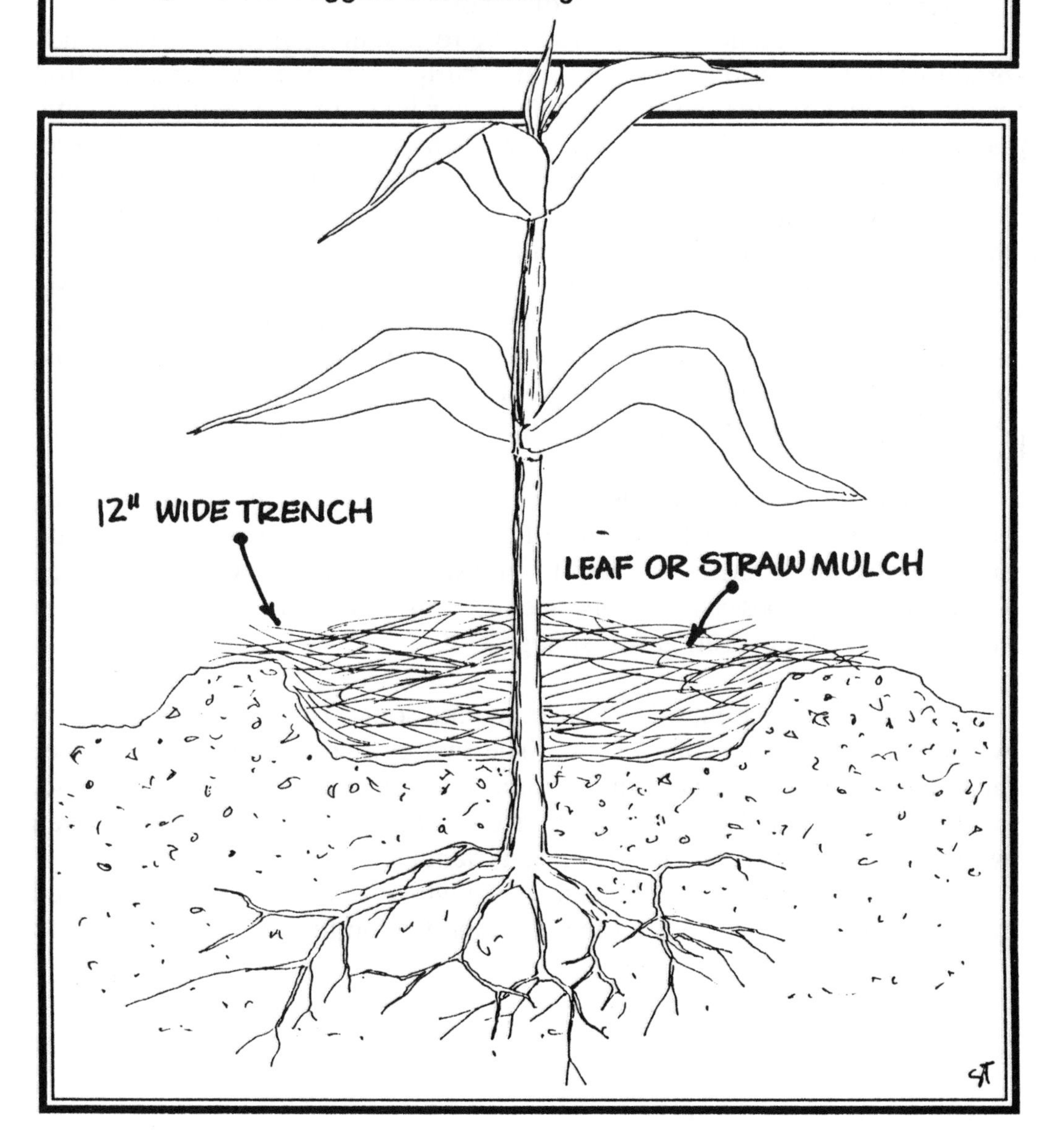

Water Storage

With full-time electricity available to operate a well-pump, the only storage required is a relatively small pressure tank. But with alternative electrical systems, full-time current in amounts sufficient to run most well-pumps may be a rarity. For this reason, most of the systems described in this discussion will have two tanks: one for storage, and the other to maintain pressure.

The size of the storage facility depends on a combination of factors, most notably the amount of water needed between refillings, the available supply (as determined by pumping and or well capacity, hauling capabilities, etc.). For example, if your water needs are about one-hundred gallons per day and your supply is a spring which produces just about that much, then a one-hundred gallon tank is the obvious choice.

Maybe that's not so obvious? We're assuming that a spring which produces 100 gallons/day is doing so at a fairly constant rate. One hundred gallons per day figures out to 4.17 gallons per hour, or .7 gallon per minute, clearly not enough of a flow-rate for even conservative household use. (Conservative water-flow from household faucets is generally between 1.5 and 3 gallons per minute.) The reason for the 100-gallon storage tank is to allow the spring to catch up with the demand.

For example, let's say you would like to do three loads of wash. Depending upon the type of machine in use, three loads of wash could easily use up a large portion of the water in a 100-gallon tank, and in just a couple of hours. A small garden sprinkler will use three or four gallons per minute. At three gallons per minute, a sprinkler will drain your tank in 33 minutes. All of a sudden, that 100-gallon tank is looking pretty small, right?

Again, thinking in terms of 100 gallons/day usage, if you are hauling your water and your truck holds five-hundred gallons, a five-hundred gallon storage tank would mean one trip to the well every five days. Unless such frequent hauling poses no inconvenience, you would be better off with a twelve or fifteen-hundred gallon storage tank.

Cisterns and ground-level tanks require some sort of system to get the water from storage to point of use. The two most basic options are either pumping the water to a smaller, elevated tank for gravity-feed to the house, or pumping directly into a pressure system. Both options are possible even with part-time power, and each has its advantages.

Cisterns offer some interesting possibilities. For the homestead located where 800-foot deep wells are the norm, and for the budget that shudders to think about multiplying that figure by the dollars-per-foot charged by your local well driller (not to mention the extravagant pump it will require to get the water out of a well of that depth), a cistern may well be the answer.

A tiny spring, a seasonal creek, a nearby watershed that carries off the snowmelt each year, a system to catch rainwater, or any combination of these, can all be directed to fill a cistern. Cisterns can be constructed at or near the water source, or the water can be pumped from the source to the cistern. A cistern can be built with enough capacity to supply a household for that part of the year that the seasonal flow is not running. Your local library will have books on the construction of cisterns.

A cistern can be an above-ground storage tank built out of concrete (ferro-cement, regular reinforced concrete, or concrete block) or a much less expensive "portable" tank. Portable tanks range from Doughboy above-ground swimming pools to tanks with sides of corrugated, galvanized iron. Either version needs a potable-water lining. Water tanks are in regular use in rain-catchment domestic water supply systems in various rainy-but-remote parts of the country.

There are many other types of water tanks, as well. Some are fiberglass, others are even stainless steel (very pricey). Fiberglass tanks may be the most practical all-around choice. They are more expensive than the Doughboy or galvanized tanks, but less expensive than concrete or ferro-cement; they last indefinitely, don't need periodic liner replacements, and can be made virtually to disappear with some creative painting and planting. Or building: we installed ours in an insulated tank house.

A concrete tank or cistern may be the most permanent but it is also the most expensive. And an underground concrete tank needs to be engineered for the soil in which it will be installed.

Another terrific water-storage device is a pond, but not necessarily for domestic water. A homestead pond has all sorts of other uses, though, like swimming, fishing, attracting wild animals and birds, and of course, aesthetics. A pond is ideal for storage of irrigation water, and it can't be beat for a fire-fighting water source if there is a permanently-installed means of getting that water (in a hurry) to any buildings you wish to protect. The uses of a pond are many, but some uses are not compatible with each other. With proper filtration, pond water might even be put to domestic use, although a small catchment for just that purpose might be easier and cheaper to implement.

Homestead ponds are a genuine asset, but building a pond requires careful consideration. Some soil types will support a pond; others require artificial methods to seal the bottom against excessive seepage. Ponds also need carefully designed and constructed spillways. We have seen beautiful ponds, that took hundreds of hours to build, lose their dams to rapid erosion, just because of an improperly designed spillway. By "rapid," we mean that a 100 foot-long, twelve-foot high dam vanished in a couple of hours once the erosion got started.

The importance of a properly constructed spillway cannot be overemphasized.

The USDA's "Ponds--Planning, Design, Construction" is one of the best publications we have found regarding the construction of ponds. It is complete, thorough and easy to understand. We recommend that anyone contemplating a pond read this one from cover to cover. (See Resource Guide.)

What Kind of "Alternative Power" Is Available?

Now, we are going to label some different types of electrical systems so we can relate systems of specific capabilities to other parts of our discussion. The labels we use here are not intended to signify universal language in the trade.

FULL-TIME 110: Other than public power, a generator-, solar-, wind-, or hydro-system running 24 hours a day and powerful enough to operate highest-demand tools, appliances, or pumps without having to start a bigger generator.

FULL-TIME LIMITED 110: A system which delivers full-time 110, but is limited to the output of its inverter during those times when the generator is not running. This system would be one which utilizes one of those state-of-the-art, high-output inverters which draw so little power at standby that it is prudent to leave it "on" 24 hours a day. Such a system would necessarily limit pump size to the smaller 110-volt pumps, and it would exclude any high-horsepower submersible pumps except during operation of the generator.

PART-TIME 110: A system in which everything--except major appliances, large tools, and pumps--runs off the 12-volt power supplied by a battery-bank, which is in turn recharged by a battery charger connected to a generator. In this kind of system, the generator must be started any time 110 power is required.

A modification of this system includes a low-priced, low-power (up to around 500 watts) inverter which is used to power small 110-volt hand tools, small kitchen appliances, sewing machines, etc. As we will discuss later, these inverters are extremely inefficient.

12-VOLT: Since a "part-time 110" system must rely on 12-volt power to pressurize the system, and even a "12-volt" system must have a generator available for occasional heavy-duty jobs, the above section, "part-time 110," applies here as well.

Any of the above systems will have a maximum amount of power available and that maximum will determine how big a pump you'll be able to operate. Maximum power available is determined in two ways: maximum power from the back-up generator, and maximum power available when the generator is off-line.

Of course, the best system in the world isn't going to bring you more water than the supply has to offer, so your decisions will be based upon a minimum of three factors: available supply, available electrical power, and water requirements.

A Discussion of Pumps

- Well pumps
  - Shallow well
  - Deep well
- Transfer pumps
  - High volume
  - High pressure
- Booster pumps
- Light-duty 110-volt pumps
  - Submersible
  - Standard
- Fire pumps
- 12-volt pumps

There are small 110-volt pumps available which can comfortably and economically handle the needs of most homes. Some will even handle the load of a garden sprinkler or washing the car. Anything more than that, such as irrigating a large garden, would require stepping up to a "real" pump, like a standard jet or booster pump.

The 12-volt pumps designed for RV use can be used in certain limited full-time applications, but their life expectancy when used full time is relatively short. We used one of the best RV pumps on the market for years in our kitchen. Its function was to deliver water from a near-ground-level tank to the kitchen sink, about a three-foot rise. The pump's performance, when operating in new condition, was adequate, but it required at least annual overhauls to keep it going. Light-duty 110-volt pumps (see Resource Guide) don't cost appreciably more, but they last almost indefinitely and produce more pressure.

The simplest all-around system for a full-time house is some version of the standard pressure-system used in most homes supplied by wells. These systems require the use of a pump which will develop at least 20 PSI (pounds per square inch) of pressure. This is about the minimum amount of pressure that will operate a standard pressure switch.

Throughout this discussion we will endeavor to design water systems capable of maintaining the 20 PSI needed to operate pressure switches and tankless water heaters.

Regardless of what kind of a system you elect to install in your home, you will probably want to have a high water-pressure capability at least occasionally, for uses such as moving water from one storage facility to another, watering a garden, washing equipment, construction uses, and so on. The options are many, but the simplest is either a light-weight electric transfer pump which you can plug into a generator (while you are charging your batteries), or a gas-engine pump.

Gas-engine pumps come in many performance ranges. Some move thousands of gallons per hour at very low pressure, and others move very little water at extremely high pressures. You must first determine what your exact needs are, and then shop for the pump which best does that job.

Well Pumps in General

Standard well pumps operate at either 110 or 220 volts AC. The type of pump required by your water system will depend upon the depth of the well, the flow of water needed, the amount of power available, and the best compromise for your particular application.

Since it is never a good idea to operate any high-draw equipment for extended periods through your inverter, we will continue on the assumption that your well pump will be in operation only when your generator is on line.

If your generator has a 220-volt output, you would be ahead to use it instead of 110 for any pump except for the smallest ones (1/3 HP or smaller). The reasons are several: a 220-volt circuit requires only one-half the amperage of a 110-volt circuit doing the same job, so there will be less heat buildup and more efficient motor operation. Also, and possibly the most important, you can use a smaller wire size when wiring your pump circuit. This becomes more important the farther the pump is from the power source.

Use the wire chart (figure 1) to determine the correct wire size for your application. The length is determined from the breaker panel or generator to the pump itself. Don't forget the length of wire necessary to reach down the well to a submersible pump.

If the water in your well never drops to a level lower than about 25 feet below the surface, you can use a shallow-well pump. These pumps are much less expensive than submersibles, and easier to install and maintain.

There are many books available on standard wells and how to set them up. Your local pump dealer may be of assistance as well. Again, we will limit our discussion here to those applications which present special problems when used with alternative electrical systems.

TABLE OF WIRE SIZES FOR 120 VOLTS SINGLE PHASE

AMPS	WATTS	NO. 14	NO. 12	NO. 10	NO. 8	NO. 6	NO. 4	NO. 2	NO. 1/0	NO. 2/0	NO. 3/0
5	600	90	140	225	360	570	910				
10	1200	45	70	115	180	285	455	725			
15	1800	30	45	70	120	190	300	480	765	960	
20	2400		35	55	90	145	225	360	575	725	915
25	3000			45	70	115	180	290	460	580	730
30	3600			35	60	95	150	240	385	485	610
40	4800				45	70	115	180	290	360	455
50	6000					55	90	145	230	290	365

FIG. 1

Transfer Pumps

Transfer pumps are designed for moving water from one place to another, and are generally portable. Some are electric, others have gas engines.

Some of the more common transfer pumps are those designed to move huge amounts of water, but at a very low pressure. These are also referred to as "trash pumps," because of their ability to pass debris that would stop or ruin a regular centrifugal pump. Their applications include filling a cistern or irrigating a field from a pond, or any other use where large amounts of water must be moved in a short period of time and the water is not being pumped more than a few feet higher than its source. Most of these pumps are gas-engine powered.

Some of the pumps we refer to in our discussion are technically not "transfer pumps," but are specific-application pumps that we just happen to have found useful to transfer water from one place to another. Hence, we call 'em transfer pumps.

Unique among these is a high-pressure pump originally intended for use in sprayers and pressure-washers. We have found these pumps useful for moving water up slopes as high as four-hundred feet in elevation. (More on this later.)

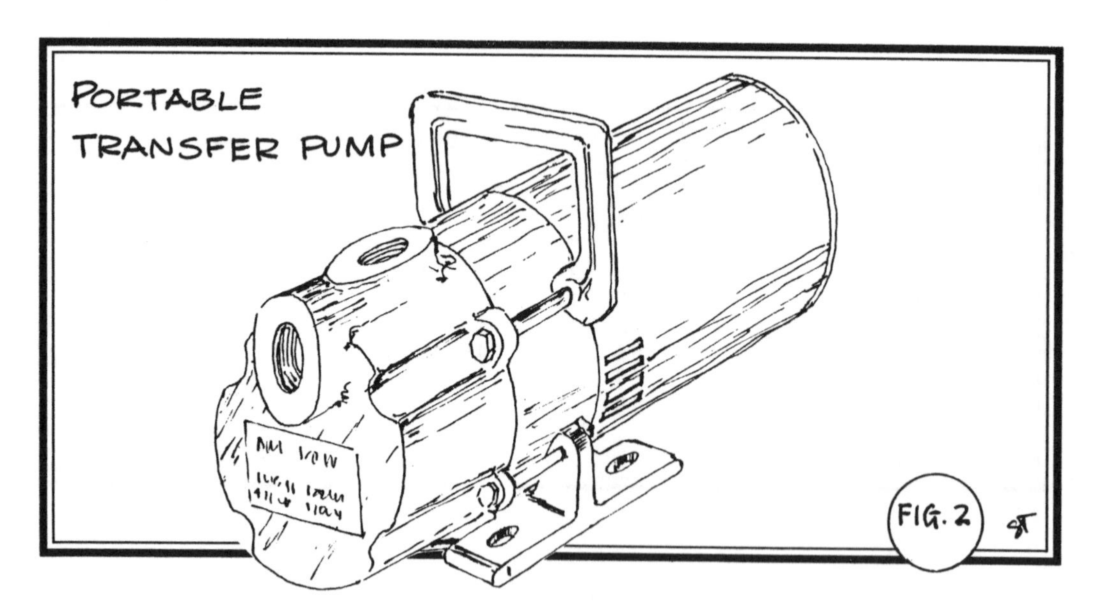

Another type of transfer pump is one we recommend for pumping water from a tank truck into a storage tank. This is a small (about 25 pounds) portable unit with a 1/3 HP electric motor and a direct-drive centrifugal pump attached. It will move up to 31 GPM (gallons per minute) or it will pump to a height of about 30 feet. However, it won't do both at the same time. As the pumping height goes up, the gallons-per-minute flow-rate goes down. For example, this same pump will deliver 21 GPM to a height of 15 feet. (See "portable transfer pump" in the Resource Guide.)

There are other variations of this pump available, too. Their specifications all vary from manufacturer to manufacturer, and model to model.

There are several small transfer pumps available that use tiny two-stroke gas engines. These are usually available in hardware or department stores. It has been our experience that these pumps require too much maintenance and do not hold up well when used for prolonged, continuous service.

Transfer pumps of all different types are of interest to folks using alternative electrical systems because of their flexibility and general usefulness. There are so many different types, however, that it is important to suit the pump to the task. Pump designs are so highly specialized that it really pays to buy a pump designed to do exactly what you need done.

There are, of course times when you will have to make compromises. For example, if your needs include pumping water to or near your house, and a small, portable electric pump would do the job, but you also occasionally need to pump from a nearby stream or spring where there is no power, and you can't justify the expense of two pumps, you might just have to go for a gas-powered pump that will do both jobs.

Another alternative, and one which works well when the remote-location pump-use is infrequent, is to use the electric pump and have on hand a small, portable generator capable of operating the pump. We used this system for years: during the several months of the year that our creek was flowing, we just left our portable 1800-watt generator and the pump in a little enclosure right by the culvert out of which we pumped the water.

This system worked especially well for us because the two-quart gas tank ran the pump for just the right amount of time to fill our 2400 gallons of water storage. When the tanks were low, we simply went to the creek, filled the pump's gas tank, started it up and forgot about it. When the pump ran out of gas, the tanks were full. Any overflow went to the garden.

Using this kind of an essentially unattended system requires that an overflow be installed in the tank to divert any excess water to a safe and useful location. Actually, an overflow should be installed in any tank in which overfilling is ever possible, which includes just about any tank.

When the creek started to dry up in late spring each year, we removed the pump and generator and used the pump to transfer water out of our tank-truck into the elevated storage tank. The portable generator was used around the homestead so often that we don't know what we would have done without it. That generator was what made it possible to use power tools to work on a piece of equipment that broke down in the back forty. Real handy.

Another important aspect of having a portable generator with an alternative electrical system is that you will have power available in the event of a breakdown (or even service/maintenance) of the main generator.

Booster Pumps

The booster pumps used in this discussion are small 110-volt units capable of developing enough pressure to operate a modest domestic water system. Booster pumps are used in cases where the pressure to any (or even all) your water system is too low. For example, if your house is supplied with gravity-fed water, and the pressure is insufficient to operate automatic on-demand water heaters, washing machines, or what-have-you, a booster pump is used to raise the pressure to a higher level.

The particular pump we used in our own system (see "booster pump" in the Resource Guide) ran well on the power supplied by our full-time-on inverter, so we left it on-line all the time. This type of setup makes for the most all-around city-like water system you can have on an alternative power system. We'll get more deeply into this particular application a little later.

Now, let's see what we can do with one of these pumps. With a gravity-feed water system that develops enough pressure for most domestic applications, but not quite enough for a good shower, a 110-volt booster pump is the answer.

If your electrical system includes a high-tech inverter that consumes almost no power at idle, you can choose a 110-volt pump which the inverter can handle, and just leave it on-line 'round the clock.

If you would rather be able to turn off this pump when not in use, Figure 8 shows how to install the pump so that it can be turned on only when required, while allowing the gravity-feed system to work normally at all other times.

The pump we used works exceptionally well with a 1200-watt inverter. It is the Dayton 1P809, available from W. W. Grainger's (see Resource

Guide). The 1P809 is a submersible pump; it must be installed either in your creek- or spring-catchment or in the bottom of your tank. We used a 1P809 as a booster pump for years in our bathroom water system. It also supplied water to the laundry and outside faucets; it drew very little power, and produced about 30 PSI pressure, enough for normal domestic needs. This pump requires an external pressure switch, and like the 12-volt pump (see below), it needs at least a small surge (captive-air) tank to minimize cycling.

We used a submersible pump in our installation because this particular pump fit our available-power/output requirements perfectly. A standard, free-standing pump that drew no more power and still produced 20 PSI would do as well.

What about shallow-well pumps used as booster units? Only the smallest can be run from an inverter (usually one-third HP or smaller). Any of these is available from any well/water pump dealer. The pumps which require the use of a generator to operate are necessarily limited to use-as-needed status (as opposed to being left on-line) in a water system running on alternative power.

We had a neighbor whose home was about four hundred feet above a crystal-clear creek from which he wished to get his water. After much research, he decided to try a high-pressure agricultural sprayer pump. Installed at the creek, it used two quarts of fuel to fill a 4000 gallon water tank at the residence. Not a bad trade-off. (See "high-pressure pump" in the Resource Guide.)

Fire Pumps

A fire pump is an undeniable asset to have on a homestead, particularly in dry country. But fire pumps are very spendy. One of the least expensive units we could find is Grainger's No. 3P636 at $2000. But anything less provides false security, letting you think you have a fire pump when, in fact, you do not.

For instance we once accumulated a six-foot tall pile of brush in a small clearing near our house. In the early spring, when the pile was still very wet, we poured a can of scrap paint down the middle and torched it. It took about ten minutes for the blaze to dry the pile out. Then it fairly exploded. The flames shot twenty-five feet in the air and the heat was intense.

We had the tank truck nearby and the pump ready to go, thinking that we were prepared to keep the heat under control. Well, we did manage to keep the surrounding trees wet enough to sustain only minor damage. But every time we aimed the stream of water in the general direction of the blaze, it evaporated before it even got close to the flames. That water supply was totally useless for serious fire-fighting.

If you pay an astronomical fire-insurance premium because you are not within a fire-protection district, you might call your insurance agent to see if there would be a significant rate adjustment if you had some effective fire-fighting equipment available. Over a few years, a lower premium could help offset the cost of the equipment.

Even the best pump won't be much use with an insufficient water supply. Take the supply available into consideration when shopping for a fire pump. A real fire pump moves at least 20 GPM of water, set at its highest pressure. Depending on the requirements at the time of use, the pump might be more effective at a lower pressure and higher volume. Then you're talking figures up to 300 GPM. (Figure out how long that would take to deplete your supply.) And if you're a believer in Murphy's Law, make sure you keep your supply topped up at all times.

Don't overlook the use of a homestead pond for your fire-fighting water-supply. The only problem might be the distance from the pond to the house. A truly effective fire-fighting system utilizing a pond needs to have a pump permanently installed at the pond, and periodic equipment-checks (as in fire drills) are essential.

Remember incompatible pond uses? Irrigation and fire-fighting are two such uses. Irrigation will draw the pond down to a dangerous level at just the time of year when the fire-danger is at its peak.

12-volt (RV) Pumps

As mentioned earlier, 12-volt RV-type pumps are intended to be used on an occasional, intermittent basis. They don't do well on a day-to-day, full-time application.

RV-type 12-volt pumps have built-in pressure switches, making installation of the pump as simple as connecting it in the line between the water source and the point of use. In an RV, that means between the water tank and the RV's points of use: kitchen faucet and the bathroom. The tank is close to the elevation of the point of use, and the water runs are short. That's what these pumps are designed for.

One of the better 12-volt RV pumps is adequate for a cabin or small home with one or two people using modest amounts of water. In this kind of use, a 12-volt pump is generally installed right in the water line, near the point of use. They all have built-in pressure switches, so in theory, no tank is required. The utility of the pump is greatly enhanced, however, with the addition of a surge tank.

RV pumps have one drawback which is annoying. An RV-type pump that is simply installed between the water source and the faucet will turn on the instant its pressure-switch detects that a faucet has been opened. As long as the faucet is opened sufficiently for the pump to produce its full capacity, the pumping will continue. The instant the faucet is closed, the pressure build-up will immediately shut off the pump. So what's the problem?

Suppose you want to open the faucet just a little: you're rinsing your toothbrush or something like that. The pressure-switch now detects the pressure drop from the opened faucet and turns on the pump. In a second or two, the pressure builds up again because the pump is designed to produce more flow than you are using, and the pump shuts off. Another second or two goes by and the pressure once more drops and the pump starts up--for a few seconds. And so on. This is called "cycling," and the resulting pulsating flow is terribly hard on the pump and the noise (if you can hear the pump) is annoying.

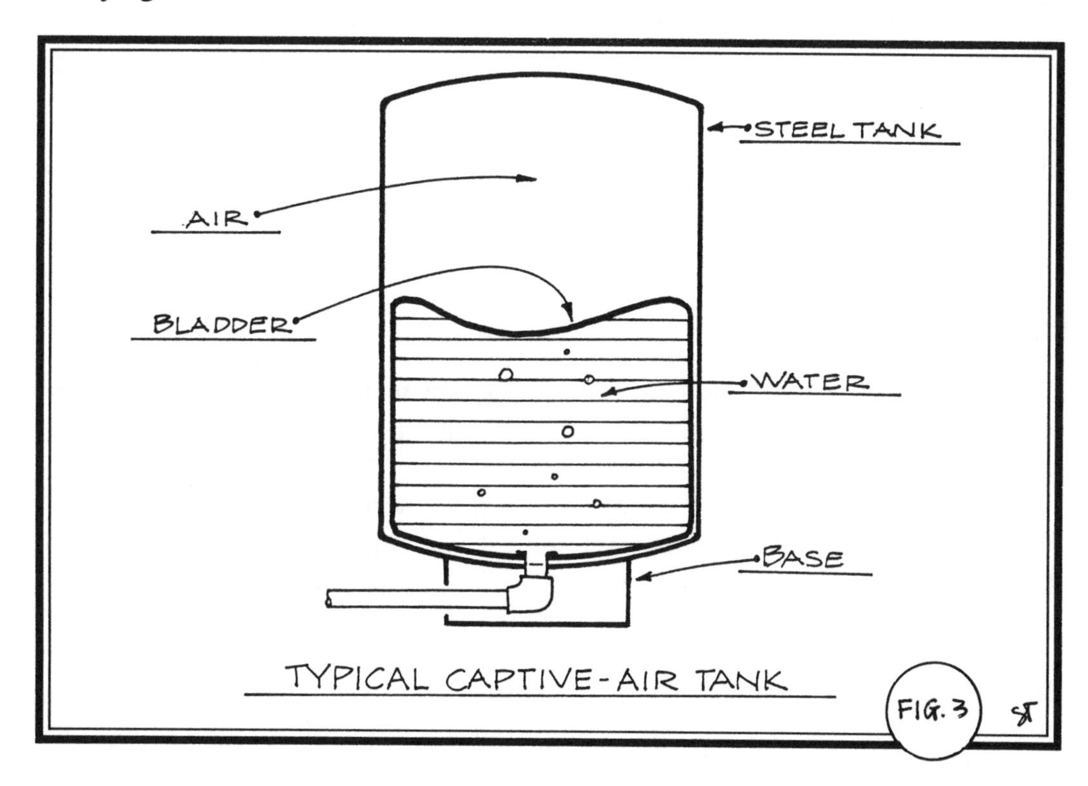

TYPICAL CAPTIVE-AIR TANK

Fortunately, it's easy to fix. Simply install a captive-air tank somewhere in the line between the pump and the first point of use. These tanks contain a bladder which keeps the pressurized air separate from the water. This prevents the absorption of the air into the water over a period of time, which causes the waterlogging problem of ordinary tanks and the then necessary periodic recharging. Captive-air tanks are well worth the extra price.

A two-gallon tank is sufficient. With the tank installed, the operation of the pump is more or less independent of turning on the faucet. For example, once the pump has pressurized the tank, you will be able to draw small amounts of water several times before the pump needs to turn on again.

Or if you need just a teaspoon of water, and if the pressure level is just low enough, the pump will turn on but will keep running for the minute or so that it takes to re-supply the tank. You can have a smooth, quiet flow of water at any flow-level, and the pump will operate at a leisurely pace, insuring its long life. These tanks are available from any water pump dealer or Grainger's.

A final note on 12-volt pumps: before you buy one, check around to see what is available. Select a pump which will deliver a minimum of three GPM and can be overhauled. That means that the pump manufacturer has been around for a while and that overhaul kits are readily available. And don't let the word "overhaul" intimidate you. Installing a diaphragm-and-seal kit is a ten-minute screwdriver job once you have removed the pump from the plumbing.

Don't Run It Dry

One of the surest ways to ruin almost any water pump is to run it dry. We burned out one very spendy deep-well submersible pump that way and then devised a system never to do it again.

No matter what your water source is, if there is any chance that you might be able to pump it out faster than it can replenish itself, you MUST install a means to prevent pumping it dry. There are two ways to accomplish this, and a combination of both is the best.

The most basic way, although not always feasible, is to select a pump that delivers slightly less volume of output than your well is capable of producing. In other words, if your well produces 20 GPM, select a pump that is rated at no more than 15 GPM. A problem arises when you start dealing with smaller volumes of water. Most well pumps pump way more than the few gallons-per-minute that may be available in some homestead situations.

Enter the gate valve.

To precisely control the output of a pump, install a gate valve on the output side and carefully adjust it so that the pump is capable of delivering a slightly lower volume of water per minute than the source is capable of producing. For example, if you know that your well will produce 6 GPM in the worst of times, adjust the valve so the pump cannot deliver more than 4 GPM.

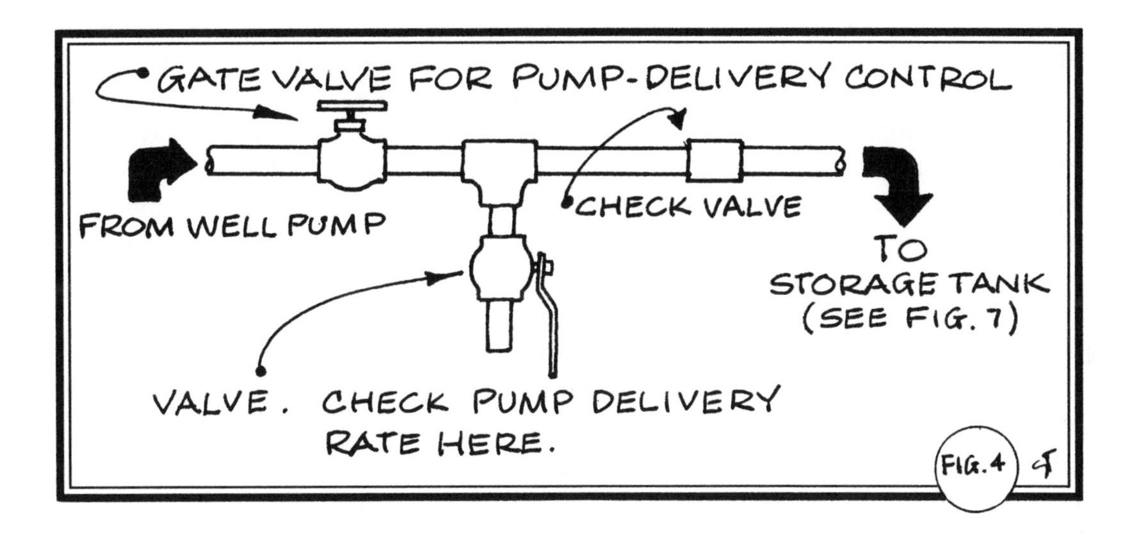

Don't cut your margin too close, either. To measure the output, fill a five gallon bucket (or any other container that you know the capacity of) and time the fill. Is still best to match the pump with the well output as closely as possible. Tell your pump dealer that you intend to close down the rate of flow with a gate valve, and to what extent. Some pumps are better suited to this application than others.

It bears repeating that your well performance figures must be taken at the lowest-production time of year. Even then, it is prudent to leave a generous reserve for those "Gee, it's never been this dry before" summers.

If your water source is a well, you probably already know what its production rate is, in gallons per minute. With any other source, such as a spring or small stream, you will have to do some experimenting to determine the flow rate.

With the suction line placed where it will normally be picking up its water, turn on the pump and carefully watch the level of water in your catchment. If the pump is capable of drawing the level down, close the valve until the source is slightly, but positively, gaining on the pump. If your water source fluctuates seasonally, as most do, you will have to monitor the situation periodically.

If you can get by year 'round on the amount of water available in the leanest time of year, just set the pump's output valve at that rate and forget it.

A gate valve is capable of very fine adjustments and is the only recommended type of valve for this application.

There is another way to protect any pump from running dry because of a slow source-recovery rate. There are submersible sensors available that will detect the presence (or absence) of water and send a signal to a relay or magnetic switch, which will then control the pump accordingly. For example, in a well with a submersible pump, the "pump-run" sensor is lowered into the well to a point somewhat above the pump. The "pump-stop" sensor is lowered to a point just above the pump.

As long as water is covering the "pump-run" sensor, the pump will run any time that the float-switch in the storage tank tells it to. As soon as the water drops below the level of the "pump-stop" sensor, the pump will stop regardless of whether or not the storage tank is full. Then as soon as the well recovers enough water, the pump will again start filling the storage tank.

These sensors can also be used in place of the float switch in the storage tank. Your pump dealer can fill you in on what is most easily available in your area. If you must deal with a lot of special-order components that are not replaceable locally, it is a good idea to have spares on hand of any parts that are critical to the operation of important systems.

Pump Noise Isolation

Whenever a water pump is installed in the house itself, rather than at a remote location like a tank- or pump-house, there is the probability of resulting pump noise in the building. Even the smallest pumps can transmit an unbelievable amount of noise if they are not properly isolated from the structure. One way to isolate a pump is to mount it on a board, preferably through any rubber mounts it may have come with, and then place the board on a thick pad of dense upholstery foam. Then use a short length of flexible hose between the pump and any rigid plumbing going to the house. RV suppliers have hoses designed to be used with potable water systems. They come in various lengths and use the same fittings as regular garden hose.

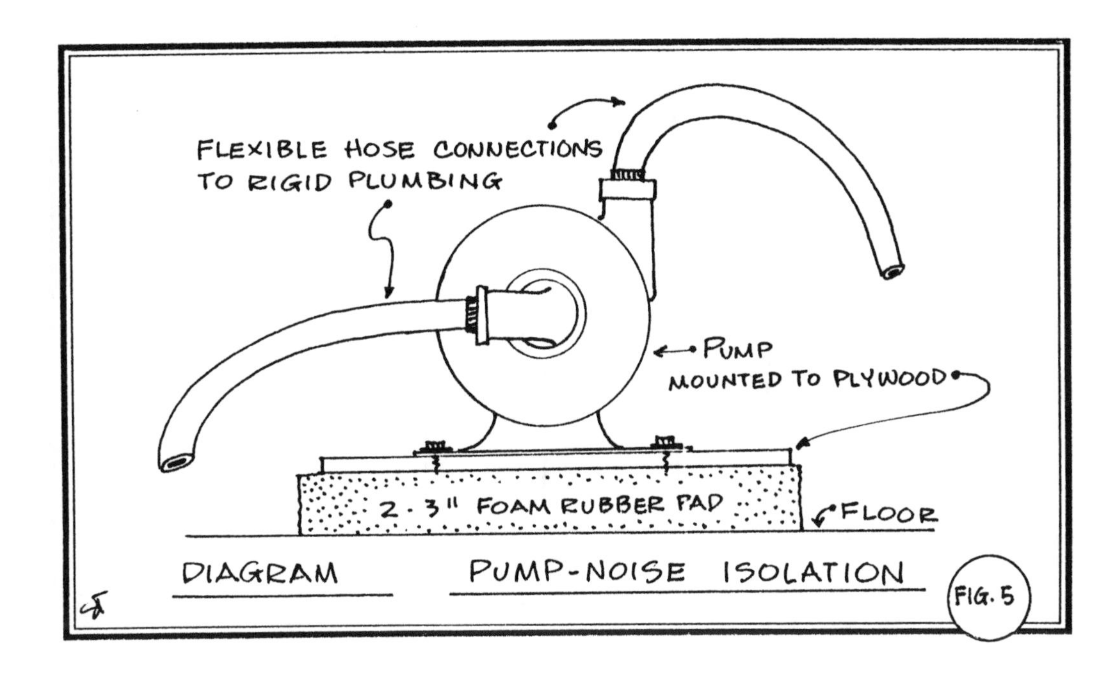

The First Specific System

Feel ready to get down to a specific typical system? Let's say you have a homestead with full-time limited 110 power and a ground-level water-source: a creek, pond, spring, cistern or other ground-level storage tank. (Remember, full-time limited 110 means 24 hour-a-day 110, but the amount of 110 is limited to the rating of the inverter whenever the generator is off-line; and the inverter is one of those hi-tech, super-efficient models.)

If the water supply and the point of use are at about the same elevation, the water can be pumped directly from the source into a conventional pressure system with a little 110-volt booster pump.

If the source is more than a foot or two lower than the point of use, the water will have to be pumped into a storage tank at or above the level of point of use, which will then supply gravity-fed water to the booster pump. The booster pump then pressurizes the system.

The size of the first pump is determined by the vertical distance the water must be pumped, and the capacity of the tank is determined by the needs of the household and by how often you will want to refill the tank.

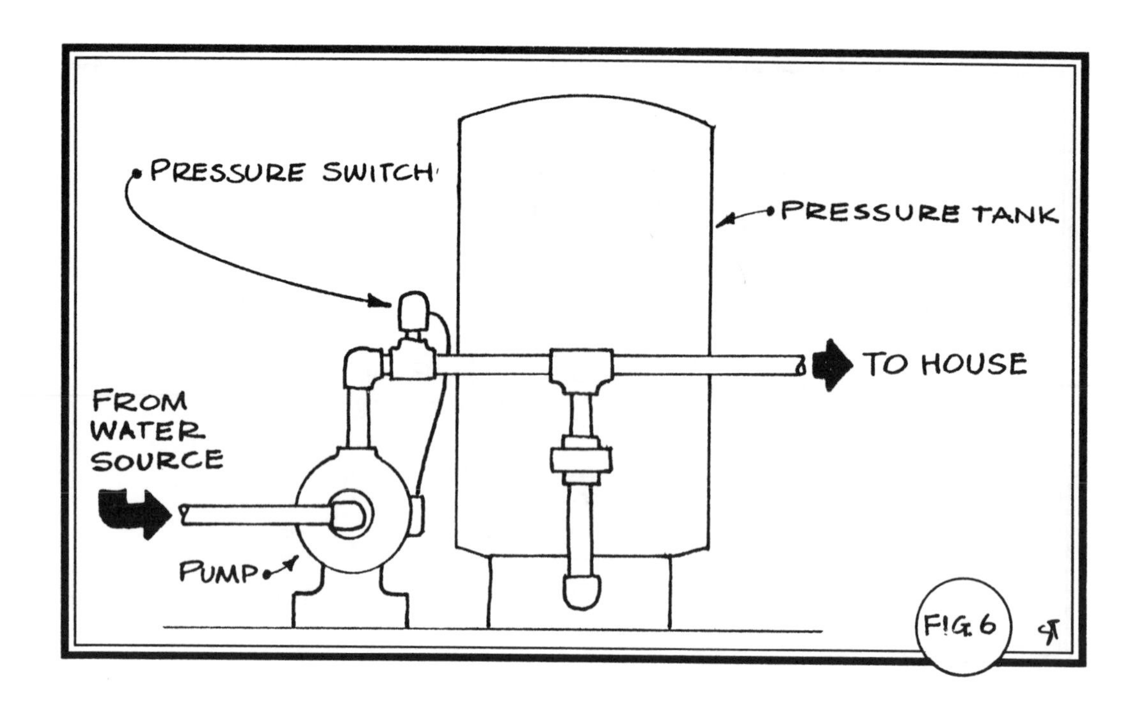

The easiest way to hook it all up is to wire the main pump directly to your generator's output, so that each time the generator comes on-line, it will automatically top off the tank as required. A float switch in the tank will shut off the pump when the tank is full.

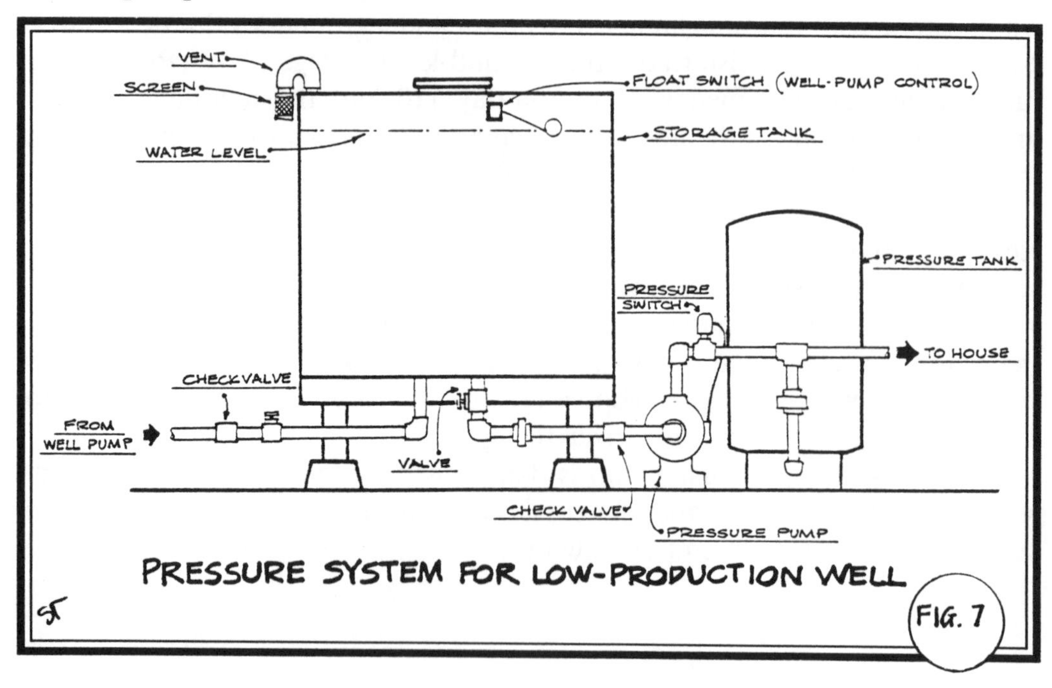

Please note that it is important to insure that the pump doesn't get power until the generator comes up to speed. Trying to start a motor while the generator is coming on-line from a dead stop is not good for the motor or the generator.

There are automatic ways to do this, too, but the simplest is to make sure that the main switch on the output of your generator is OFF while you are starting the generator, and stays off until the generator is happily running at its normal speed. (See "Resource Guide" for MORE POWER TO YOU! which tells how to do this automatically in remote-start generator systems.)

If the source is higher than the point of use, a catchment of some sort will be required from which the booster pump can draw its water. The only instance in which this catchment need be bigger than just enough to draw water out of is if the source is a spring or stream which won't keep up with the pump. And that would have to be a very small stream.

If the source is very clean running water, the catchment can be nothing more than a five-gallon plastic pail. If there is a possibility of sediment or other debris in the water supply, the catchment must have some means of filtering the water or at the very least be large enough to allow the impurities to settle out. Ordinary clean sand makes an excellent filtering medium.

Another Typical System

Let's run through another typical water system and see how it can be operated with power supplied from an alternative source. This system draws its water from a spring at a point ten feet higher than the average faucet-level in the house. Obviously, this system could get by with no pumps at all, but with ten feet of drop, you would have only about 5 PSI of water pressure. The alternatives are several:

1. Simply use just the gravity-feed pressure and design the system around that limitation. The water heater (necessarily a tank-type) would best be installed at a level higher than point of use, and any shower head would have to be one of those big, old-fashioned ones designed for low pressure. Neither the new low-volume shower heads nor an on-demand water heater would work with this system.

2. With a part-time 110 or 12-volt electrical system, use gravity-feed pressure wherever it is adequate, and use a small pump, either 12-volt or the 110-volt unit described above for those applications requiring more pressure. The pump can then be switched on only when needed, as for a shower. (See Fig. 8.)

3. With a part-time or full-time 110 electrical system, use gravity-feed to supply water to a standard pressure system. This would require that the pump, which is controlled by a pressure switch, be left on-line 'round the clock. This system works well with an inverter that is "on" all the time. (See Fig. 6.)

Of the three systems, obviously the first would use the least electrical power (none), and it would be the most limited in present function and future adaptability.

The second system is the most conservative and is limited only in that water-pressure would be low in any part of the system that is still gravity-fed. If you are comfortable with having your faucets run at a leisurely pace, this would be the way to go.

If you feel a need for city-like water-pressure in all areas of your home, then the third system is the one to use.

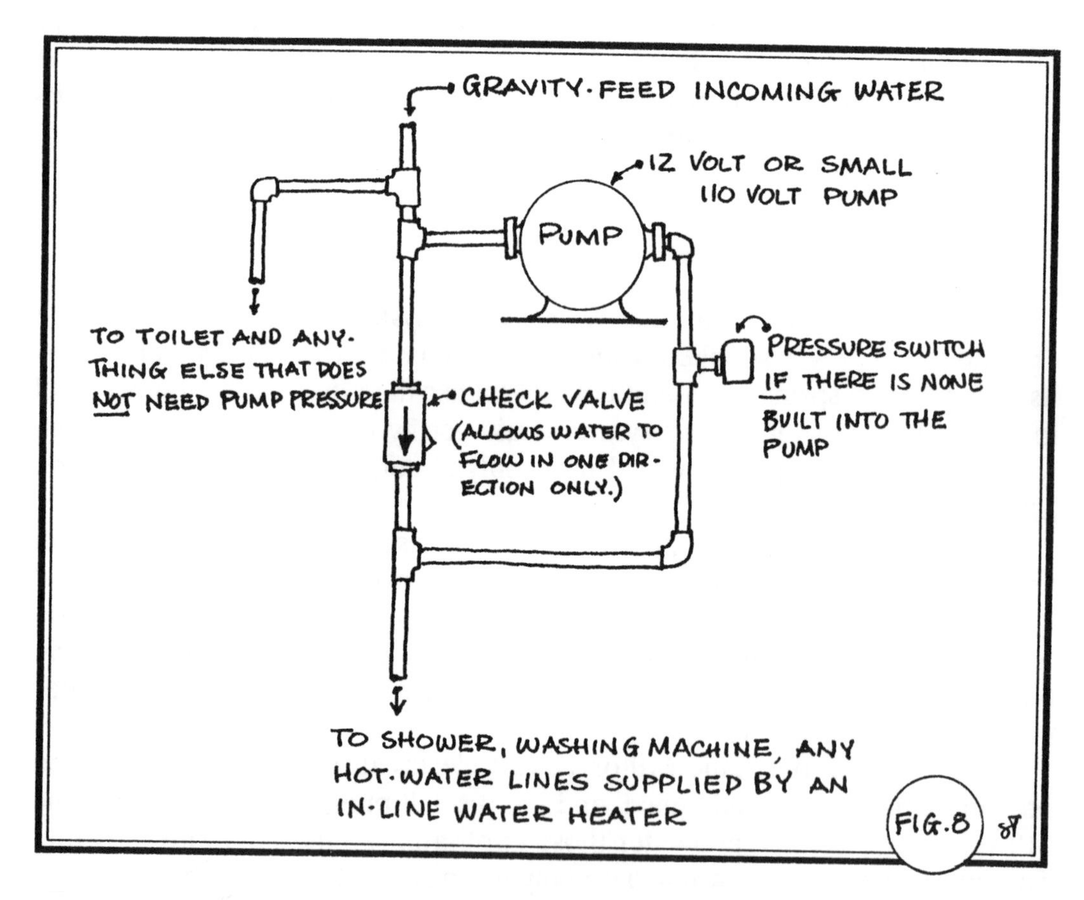

FIG. 8

Depending on the size of your home and the complexity of your water system, a full-time system like the third option will require a more substantial pump than would be necessary in the second system. More substantial pumps draw more power, require bigger inverters, bigger wires, and more storage capacity in your batteries. A 12-volt (RV-type) pump at each point of use requiring the higher pressure is an option, but only as a last resort, because of the high prices and mortality rates of 12-volt pumps. These are all factors that must be considered when designing the system. (See "Phantom Loads and Inverters" in Chapter 11.)

Water Heaters, Conventional...

A conventional gas-fired or electric water heater is merely a large tank with a built-in heater and a thermostat. Of course, using a conventional electric water heater assumes that you have full-time 220-volt power to run it. Conventional heaters keep the entire tankful of water hot at all times to allow you the convenience of drawing off a little hot water whenever you wish.

Even if you use no hot water for extended periods of time, the heated water in the tank eventually cools down anyway, and the thermostat turns the heater back on. In a gas-fired unit, the thermostat opens the gas valve to light the burner; in an electric heater, the thermostat turns on the heating elements. Keeping water hot all the time is an expensive extravagance.

An excellent way to cut the costs of operating an electric water heater is to install a timer that turns the heater on only for the few minutes required to heat the water you will be using. For example, the water heater in our current (temporary) home turns on at 5:00 PM, and stays on only for the fifteen minutes required to fully heat its stored water. This is enough water to get through preparing supper, washing the dishes, and showers. At 5:00 AM, it turns on for another fifteen minutes, supplying hot water for the morning-shower folks and doing the breakfast dishes.

We used to run only the evening cycle, but after our seventeen-year-old's morning shower, there wasn't quite enough hot water to get through the day. There is no noticeable performance difference between operating the water heater for two fifteen-minute cycles and leaving it on 24 hours a day. The electricity savings, however, are significant. The timer that makes it work is listed in the Resource Guide.

The timer principle can be used with a part-time alternative system, too, by turning on the water heater for fifteen or twenty minutes while the generator is running.

In our opinion, any use of an electric or gas-fired tank-type water heater is to be discouraged, and the above concepts are discussed as temporary measures only. If you do ever operate a tank-type electric heater on a part-time system, make certain that your generator has the capacity to run the water heater and whatever else will be on at the same time. Also, make sure that the heater is never "on" when the generator is started.

...and Tankless

An in-line, or tankless water heater stores no water at all. It consists of a small gas burner which heats water as it passes through a series of loops in the heater, and a gas valve which turns on the burner when it senses a drop in water pressure. The instant you turn on your hot water faucet, the resulting pressure-drop turns on the burner, heating only the water that passes through the heater. The instant the faucet is closed, the gas valve also closes and the heater shuts off.

These heaters are so efficient that the amount of fuel they use is almost insignificant. Of course, there's a catch. In-line water heaters are relatively expensive. The least expensive models are those intended for RV use. Unlike RV water pumps, however, they are not prone to premature failure from heavy use.

We used two Paloma in-line water heaters on our homestead on the mountain: one in the kitchen and another in the bathroom and laundry. We used two heaters because the distance between the bathroom and the kitchen was significant and we wanted to be able to take a shower without someone freezing us out by turning on the kitchen water. Both heaters still functioned as-new after ten years of daily use.

The only limitation of the RV-type heaters is that they are designed to deliver the kind of flow-rates consistent with RV usage: low. Showers will be rain-like, and it will take a little longer to fill the sink or tub. If that doesn't bother you, they are well worth investigating.

To be used to its fullest advantage, any in-line heater should be installed as close to its point of use as possible. That way you get hot water almost instantly.

The larger tankless heaters (of which Paloma also makes a line), which are intended for regular domestic use, cost about twice as much (or more) than the RV models, but ONE would serve in a well-designed home. (We feel that a good design incorporates placing all the rooms that include plumbing--bath, kitchen, laundry--conveniently close together to keep plumbing runs as short as possible.) On-demand tankless water heaters are available in several sizes, with much higher flow-rates than the RV units. They are available from the alternative energy dealers in the Resource Guide.

Valves, Hoses, and Other Water-line Restrictions

If you're like most of us and can use all the water-pressure you can get (particularly from a low-power system), you must pay attention to the many things in a water system which can act as restrictions. Among them are rough and corroded pipes, less-than-optimum-sized pipes, valves incorrect to their applications, excessive and/or poorly planned fittings, and poorly planned pipe routing which causes more bends and sharp corners than necessary.

The problems caused by excessive bends and corners are easily recognized, and much easier to address when installing a new system than to correct in an existing one. The shortest and most efficient path between two points is always a straight line. Straight lines in plumbing circuits are seldom possible, so compromises must be made. Copper and plastic pipe fittings are designed to have almost no internal ridges that can cause flow-resistance, so given enough space, it would be better to use two 45° bends than one 90° elbow in a situation where maximum flow is critical.

Copper pipe can also be bent into easy-flowing corners. This requires the use of a special pipe bender ($20-$35 new), and if you're going to plumb a whole house, it would be a good investment. Pipe benders are available at most well-supplied hardware stores, plumbing-supply houses, or catalog stores such as Grainger's.

Iron pipe is better avoided altogether if pressure and flow are critical. Iron pipe is rough on the inside, and the fittings leave gaps and shoulders exposed to the flow of water.

Valves are perhaps the biggest flow-restrictors in most water systems. Common "globe" valves, which are the least expensive ones your supplier will have on hand, have inside them several sharp turns and the necessarily narrow passageways. They offer high restriction and should not be used anywhere where flow-rate is critical. The two best valves are gate- and ball-valves.

Gate valves, as their name implies, use a "gate" that moves completely out of the flow-path when the valve is fully opened. Ball valves use a ball with a hole through the middle. The valve is turned off by turning the handle 90°, which turns the hole in the ball crosswise to the flow path.

Both types offer almost no resistance to water flow when opened fully. Gate valves are usually slightly less expensive, but require a lot of turning to open and close. Ball valves require only a 90° turn of the handle, so they are especially well suited to applications where a valve must be opened and closed often.

Standard residential plumbing calls for 1/2" pipe to be used almost everywhere inside the house, except for the bigger feeders that supply more than one 1/2" leg. This works just fine for most alternative-energy-operated water systems, too.

If you find yourself with long runs of pipe to get your water from one place to another, 1" plastic pipe is a good choice. Plastic pipe offers the least flow resistance, and is certainly the easiest material to use. It is also (and this doesn't happen very often) the cheapest. Check your local codes.

Beware of using pipe too small. Some pumps will not operate at anywhere near their rated performance levels if their inlet and/or outlet fittings are reduced to accommodate smaller pipe or hose. This is particularly true of the high-volume, low-pressure pumps designed to move thousands of gallons per hour through their 2" and bigger openings. Throttled down to garden-hose size, these pumps will do well to produce ten per cent of their rated output.

Cold Weather Considerations

If you happen to live in the tropics, you can skip this part. But if the temperature in your area *ever* gets down into the low thirties, read on.

All water systems installed in cold climates must be protected from freezing. The ways to accomplish this are several, but your local building codes will dictate what is allowed in your area.

The most effective method we have found to protect the sub-floor area is to thoroughly insulate the perimeter of the crawl space (i.e., the inside of the foundation walls) of your home and do not insulate under the floor. It has been our experience that this method allows the small amount of heat-loss getting through the floor to keep the entire crawl-space from freezing.

In our own home, the temperature in the crawl-space never went much below 40° even when the outside temp dropped down below zero. An additional benefit to this setup is that the floor was always warm and the house heated much more evenly. Heat-loss to the ground was insignificant, because the ground temperature a few inches down was about 40° anyway. If heat-loss to the ground is a factor in your area, an insulation blanket directly on the ground will solve that problem.

Then the Oregon building officials, in their infinite wisdom, decided that we could no longer insulate houses in this manner. The new code stipulated R-25 insulation in the floor and asked for none around the perimeter of the foundation. With this change, all of the subfloor plumbing hanging below the level of the insulation (most of it) was directly in the icy air of winter. About the only way to protect this exposed plumbing is to wrap it with heat tape and then with insulation.

Heat tape, an electrical resistance-heat element that looks like a long, flat extension cord, is controlled by a thermostat. When the temperature drops below a pre-set level, the heat tape turns on and keeps the pipes from freezing. The exposed plumbing is wrapped with a generous layer of insulation after installing the heat tape. Insulation alone will help keep the pipes from freezing only for short durations of slightly sub-freezing temperatures, and it isn't wise to depend on it even for that.

Of course, the use of heat tape presumes that you have the necessary 'round the clock 110 power to operate it. If you don't, or if you choose not to use your available power in such a manner, you'll have to design your plumbing a little differently from the normal house.

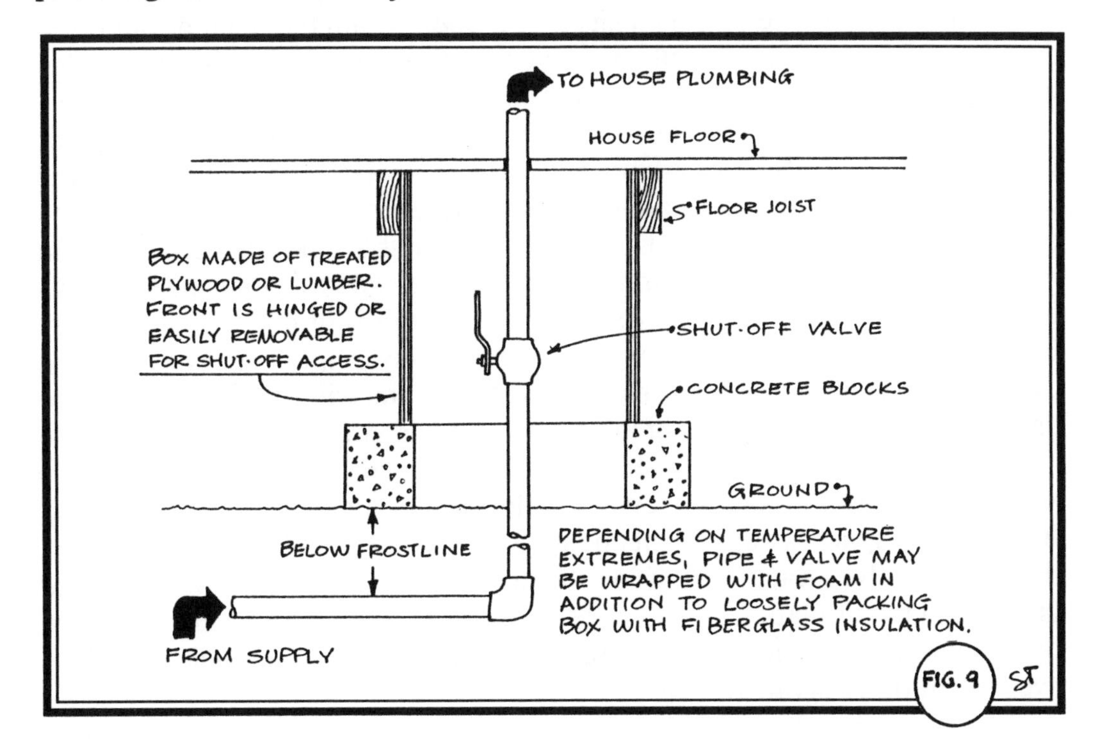

A fairly easy way to accomplish this if you haven't designed your house yet, is to run one pipe from your water supply into the house through a special box attached to the bottom of the house floor, and then packed with insulation. (See Figure 9.) All the rest of the plumbing is then run through interior walls of the house. If you must install plumbing fixtures on exterior walls, like, for example, a bathroom sink, the sink should be installed in such a way that the supply line can be routed from an adjacent interior wall.

If this sounds a little fanatical, listen to this: in our house on the mountain, we insulated the crawl-space perimeter walls and ran our plumbing under the floor as described above. The only problem we ever had with freezing plumbing was a short length of pipe that came up through the floor and was routed inside of the exterior wall up to the bathroom sink. Even with the fiberglass insulation in the wall, the pipe froze inside the wall. We re-routed that short length of pipe to run up the inside of the wall inside of the vanity cabinet. End of problem.

Outside faucets are easy. Your local plumbing supply can supply you with freeze-proof faucets for just that purpose. They look and work like regular faucets, but the actual mechanism is deep within the building, and they are designed to drain out all the water between the valve itself and the exterior faucet every time the faucet is turned off.

Every cold-country plumbing system (particularly those with sub-floor plumbing runs) needs a low-point drain. This is a valve that is installed at the lowest point in the building's plumbing, so that when opened, it will drain the entire system. It important that all of the plumbing be installed to drain toward this valve, and particular attention must be paid to avoid any low spots in which water can still stand even after the system is drained. The primary function of this drain is to enable you to completely empty your system if you ever need to leave your house unattended during the winter. (Don't forget to empty toilet bowls and tanks of all water if there's any chance they'll freeze.)

The main shut-off valve from the supply to the house should be easily accessible in case of an emergency (read: sudden major leak in the house). If your crawl-space is kept warm enough to keep the plumbing from freezing, the valve can be located just inside the access door. If not, the valve can be installed in the insulation box described above. The least likely valve to freeze up is a ball-valve. The normally used gate-valves can get impossible to close even when only slightly frozen.

(We like to have a crawl-space access door inside the house, as in a closet floor. That way, if you ever need to get to the shut-off valve quickly, you don't have to worry about trying to deal with an access door that's either frozen shut or buried in snow.)

In our installation, our 1200 gallon supply tank was in a building only ten feet from the house. The tank house was thoroughly insulated, and in all but the longest cold spells, the thermal mass of all that water kept the tank house from freezing. We installed our main shutoff valve right on the outlet of the tank. When the temperature stayed down in the zero-and-below range for any amount of time, we turned on the small electric heater in the tank house. The heater came on automatically whenever the generator was running, and this was enough to keep anything from freezing. It should be noted, however, that this system required that the water level be kept topped up at all times to ensure the necessary thermal mass.

Getting in a hurry and cutting corners while designing and building your system means you'll be chasing down the glitches forever. When you design your system, make sure that your pumps are of sufficient size and power to handle their intended jobs, that the pipe runs are big enough and free-flowing, and that all connections are made carefully and thoroughly. Pressure-test all parts of the system before sealing any of it behind drywall or paneling. A carefully thought-out and well-crafted water system is a genuine asset to any homestead.

Hauling Water

Hauling water doesn't have to be the hassle it would seem to be at first glance. We did it for ten years, and after the system got streamlined a bit, it wasn't bad at all.

Our source was an artesian well on the road to town, and from the start, we did our best to combine our water-trips with supply or grocery runs. We just used the water truck for our town run and filled the tank on the way home.

We started out hauling water with six 55-gallon drums on the back of our 3/4-ton pickup. After a few years of dealing with the inconvenience of pumping water out of six individual drums we bought an old-but-trusty two-ton flat-bed truck and mounted a 550-gallon water tank to its ten-foot bed. The tank was mounted crosswise, right behind the cab in wooden saddles and was securely chained to the frame of the truck. The truck was plenty stout enough for its load, but small enough that so it wasn't a big deal to drive it to town.

Having a single large tank makes pumping the water a snap. Just hook up the hose and turn on the pump. Time the operation the first time around, and from then on, set a timer as soon as you start the pump. When the timer goes off, you have time to turn off the pump before the tank runs dry.

We were pumping water to an elevated tank so it took us about twenty minutes to pump out the 550 gallons. We had a neighbor whose tank was below the level of his driveway and he didn't even need a pump.

Should you want to build a first-class water-hauler, excellent sources of good, heavy-duty trucks at bargain prices are the truck-rental companies. For example, U-Haul fleets are well maintained and get retired from service with lots of life left in them. Their moving vans are often relieved of their boxes and then sold as cab-and-chassis units; just the ticket for a water-hauler. These trucks sell for as little as $800 in great condition.

Tanks can often be found at farm auctions or at farm-machinery and supply outfits, or you can find your nearest manufacturer listed in the Yellow Pages. The cost depends on how fancy you want to go with potable-water linings, but the tanks themselves are surprisingly inexpensive.

Another convenience you might want to consider is to install your pump on your truck; we did, and it proved to be really handy. Our only problem was that our roads got very dusty in the summertime, and even with a cover on the pump, it was impossible to keep dust out of the motor. If you don't have the dust problem, the truck-mounted pump is worth considering.

After removing the pump from our truck again, we installed it under the house in such a way that it could be easily reached from a small access door from the outside. This way it never got cold enough to have to drain it after each winter use, and pumping out the truck was as easy as connecting a hose and turning on a switch.

Hauled water, no matter how wonderful a system you have for hauling it, does bring with it the motivation for frugality. You will learn to conserve if you haul your water.

[Footnote to Chapter 13: The portable transfer pump mentioned on page 114 is Grainger's No. 1P862. The fire pump (p. 117) is No. 3P636. The wonderful little 110-volt submersible pump (p. 117) is No. 1P809. The high-pressure sprayer pump (pp. 114, 117) is a Sears 71AF46121N High Pressure twin-piston sprayer, 500psi/3gpm. An alternative is their 71AF46131N roller pump, 150psi/5gp. Other alternatives are often available from Northern Hydraulics; check their catalog. RV-type in-line water heaters (p. 128) are available through most RV dealers. The brand we had such good luck with was Paloma. Water-heater timer is an Intermatic "Little Gray Box" available from Grainger and other electrical dealers.]

S.C.

Elaine's Chapter

You may have noticed that we often recommend getting more than one opinion when seeking important information. Well, in an effort to avoid having this entire book be based on our personal feelings and the results of our own observations, we would like to introduce a very dear friend and former neighbor, Elaine.

Elaine and her partner of twenty-one years have been serious and successful homesteaders since the 1970's. They are living in what started out as an old abandoned homestead on about eighty acres of north central Oregon. They've fixed up one of the old buildings and made it into a cozy, comfortable, compact home. They built a barn, did a lot of planting of both the ornamental and edible varieties, and are now in the middle of an ambitious project: building their own home from mostly salvaged materials. They build as they can afford to; no mortgages here.

We have been bugging Elaine for quite a while to put her thoughts on paper. She is basically a private person, and although we have enjoyed countless hours discussing very personal things, putting them on paper seemed to her to transcend her realm of "private."

Elaine and we disagree on some points (like the desirability of having your own electrical system) but our basic philosophies are much the same. She believes in total honesty, and is more comfortable in her communication with the earth and its natural environs than anyone else we know.

We asked Elaine to give us her thoughts on what it takes to be a successful homesteader; what it takes to be as peaceful and content as she is with her spot on the planet and her place in humanity. What follows is what she wrote.

Dear Skip,

You asked for a chapter to a book you're tending to write and you well know I've not been what you'd call overly enthusiastic about doing such. But you're a good friend of mine and I'll give it a go.

It's not that I don't always have a load of opinions or that I'm shy about them, but I'm bright enough to know you've got to keep your opinions and philosophy to yourself a whole lot of the time if you hope to have any friends....

I'm happy and pretty well proud of who I am as an individual because I think I really do believe in the stuff I say, 'cept maybe when I've had a glass one too many. But even then the truth probably will come out, truth be told. So in this here endeavor I tell it like it is for me, and the way I think it should be. I've learned tolerance, but it don't mean that I necessarily agree with all such that I tolerate.

Philosophically speaking (and Philosophy is where it's at if anyone is to be successful at what it is they do), I truly couldn't live anywhere else except very intimately connected to the land. Well, I could, but I would turn my city lot into a homestead also, so you see it's more a state of mind than a piece of territory.

What living in the outback affords me is more freedom for that which I already am. If I want to crank up the speakers at whatever time, it don't bother no neighbors. I pee where I want to when I got to. If it's too hot, I take off my shirt and don't have to worry about offending anyone or getting hauled off to the hoosegow.

If I want to get a little tanked and ponder the mysteries of life, I can drive out into the woods and not worry about hurting someone. You know that I strongly disagree with driving drunk in the civilized world, but every once in a while a folk gets a little mortalized and you need to play it where it goes. You can't do this without getting in trouble, except where I live.

So to live successfully on the land is a pretty simple question for me: if not here, where? I so truly value my freedom, I would choose over anything else to have it. Even if I don't use it every day, I know, I mean *really know* it's here. Kinda like the dude in jail, he don't ever forget he's in jail. Well, I don't ever forget the humongous amounts of freedom I'm availed of.

And yes, there is chicken-spit stuff, like politics, land-use planning, clear-cutting, inequalities of all sorts, rape, murder and mayhem that could make my day, but there just ain't much that I can do about them. These peoples ain't read their history, else they'd know it ain't gonna be much different if you rip your guts out about it or not.

It's hard to be a country activist because when the sun comes up it doesn't set on any of the above. Pure and simple. If I would let it get to me and the stuff came to my door, I would deal with it appropriately: shoot the big toes off the scumbags and give refuge to those that need it. That's in my control. But I'd more than likely end up doing a stretch in the Grey-Bar Hotel in the big city for the same good thoughts. Another reason for living where I do.

It ain't hard to see how I am successful at living where I do when you look at the philosophies of living in general.

A body's mindset is the single most important thing to living on the land. It's different for others, I suppose.

I've read some of those homesteader books which a great many of them write because they need the money. "Living Off The Land and Variations on a Theme." There ain't a soul in this modern world of the US of A (well a few) who live off the land, surely not in the lower 48. More correct is live ON the land, and bring money. Most of the failure, as I see it, is lack of MONEY. If you spend $2000 a month in the city, what the hell motivates a person to think they can live on less out in the country when they are further away from a town with increased fuel expenses, not as much competition with local business, hence everything is more expensive?

If a person (usually it's only one; they drag the other along) is seriously considering moving from the urban environs out to the remote, they should practice, practice, practice first. Right the hell where they're at. This is not a kind approach, but neither is it doomed to failure. If you can't homestead in the city, you sure as spit ain't gonna be able to do it in the country, not in the long run.

I'm talking longevity here, more than five years. Gee, more than most relationships last . . . maybe I am in an unreal world. Well, back to the city and the first steps.

1. Cut your income to minimum wage standards - 40 hr/wk.

2. Grow and can your own food.

3. Sew your own clothes, or practice Goodwill Shopping.

4. Build your dream house in miniature for a kid's playhouse (keep track of expenses; it'll blow you over).

5. Buy yourself an old Subaru 4X4 and do the work on it yourself. (You'll have to when the snow is ass-deep to an elk. It's the only time motor vehicles seriously fail.)

6. Shut your water off. (What! How am I gonna grow a garden? Good question. Cheap land, that you can afford, is already gone. What is left, don't have water.) Ponder how you will do all the above, plus keep tidily clean hauling all your water.

7. Electricity--well, Skip, I know you and I personally disagree on this point, but as one who don't hardly know one end of a light bulb from the other, I say--Hook to the Grid! You can get burned out quick on home-brewed kilowatts. It is a challenge exciting, terrifically rewarding when it succeeds, but if you ain't already brewed your own kilowatts in your city back yard, consider this very carefully when you read ads for property without electricity.

8. To all female types whose male types have assured them all of the above is easy: Beg, borrow, steal (maybe try the library) Carla Emery's *Old Fashioned Recipe Book.*

9. Health Insurance. Well, what about it?

10. Kids! A whole different program on back to the land. They can become miserable nasty little tyrants insisting on, well most everything we wanted when we were kids; friends, burgers, movies, hangin' out (not amongst the deer and the antelopes). Don't know how you handle this one exactly, don't know anyone who has, but it bears major consideration which should be done within confines of the present situation. Remember, what is viewed as freedom to an adult is not at all the same to a teenager. Trust me.

Okay, so how will you know when you're ready to move to the land? If you have survived the above ten steps for a full year, and still have money in the bank in spite of your reduced income (and lowered standard of living), then do it.

Life out here in the country is good. I think it is the only way to truly live fully for the freedom-minded type. But bear in mind money ain't something you find, and if you don't have it, the same problems that beset you in the urban environs will descend upon you as a swarm of locusts in the outback.

Here are some Rules.

1. You always carry your baggage with you. Translation: Location doesn't necessarily make for happiness.

2. There is never enough money for those who need more.

3. If there's two of you, one back won't carry it all.

4. If you can't do it where you're at, you won't where you're going.

5. Visits from urban friends are few and far between, then none.

6. The tasks are many, the work hard and seemingly endless.

7. You need to have a source of monthly income.

8. You will not succeed if you do not follow the other seven.

This might sound a little harsh, but it's the real world the way I see it; and I've seen it go by for more than just a few "back to the landers." Perhaps it would have been good for them to read something other than "you can do it" books, for this, after all, is not Nike® land.

On the other hand, I once had a friend (who is no longer living in the country) tell me I never gave her a good piece of advice. The way I see it, a fool wouldn't know a good piece of advice if it bit her in the butt, and I wasn't willing to go that far.

There are the folks who know it all, and I mean *know it all*. They never done anything to amount to anything, but read a passel of books, and they got an answer for everything. And then there is those poor fools that were standing behind the door when the Good Lord passed out the common sense. These you really just got to walk away from. They're beyond help because the only sound they hear, or want to hear is their own voice.

I've known a few of these folks and they're terrible frustrating. It's not like they're a balloon and you could just stick 'em and let some air out (though I've oft wished for a sharp needle to poke some pin head with). But you know it takes a lot of gall to tell someone who's living out on the land and enjoying it, how it is they really ought to be doing it. They got no humility.

And if you don't have humility, Mother Nature will break your butt. A successful country folk has got lots of humility. They've learned it through the years. They know that most of the time success is give-and-take, opportunity knocks, that sort of thing. Course, these are country folks I'm talking about, so they already got sense and already worked damn hard for their stripes.

I got my first lesson in fools and egotists when I was a lot younger on the ranch in southern Oregon--was about that time in the 60's when Oregon got discovered by the Californians. (Sorry, Skip, but 'tis true.) So anyway, this big-shot dude wearing chaps and posting his horses on the asphalt rides by the gate. He's the new owner of three of our neighbors' old ranches. He was vice president of San Jose Steel, he said. Well, bow down and kiss the earth, I guess. I did not.

So he launches onto what would become his weekly dissertations on what the hell we were doing wrong as farmers and how it was that he was now in possession of our neighbors' ranches 'cause he really, really knew how to raise cows. You can tell this left an impression on me. So I'd look up from the shovel on the weekends when he'd come posting by with the new wife (he was only a weekender, you see; had to run the company nine-to-five the other five. He had a hired man--a good man, but a poor bastard that got put through hell so he could support his family).

Well, the V.P. lasted about five years before he lost all the ranches, all the equipment--the whole Mary Ann. You see, he'd paid more for all three ranches than any kind of one-calf cow could ever have brought in. He did not have any kind of humility and that lesson didn't humble him. It broke him in all senses. Being humble might have saved him the grief, but he'd've needed a brain transplant to receive it.

This is an important little story, not just because it's true, but because it delineates what constitutes a mean little toad posting down a road. You never know when you're gonna run into them. But of course, you're really never prepared for it. My partner thinks my naivete for people is only exceeded by my patience to listen to their dreams. So I will still to this day try to guide these fools who come through my front gate during the mud season in their two-wheel-drives wondering where it is they need to be.

Maybe it's that I don't have enough humility myself, and stand supreme in the ruts they leave behind, only because I'm not lost. We can all use a little studying in the humble department. Just not being lost ain't something to be real proud of, necessarily.

I'm still trying to figure out what magic makes me still here on this piece of earth. A person maybe needs some kind of mystic experience--more than we want to allow these days--getting imbued with spirit. I'm not talking about born-again, out-of-control, handing-it-over-to-a-higher-power kind of spirit. For me, maybe it was my Uncle Jack.

Uncle Jack wasn't even my uncle. I adopted him. He didn't have any kids of his own, so he didn't mind. He taught me, oh, so many things as I think on it. But mostly he pulled my worth out and made me supremely confident of my ability to survive in the woods, and be proud of it.

Now, as a young girl, I got to know that, although Uncle Jack's lessons were great, they weren't worth spit in the real world of boys and girls. The woods won out in the long run, but I paid a few dues in the interim. Kids are not kind, never will be, 'cause they are raised by parents who are unkind. It is as it is. So, though I had some less than happy times when I was younger, I always had a kind of anchor, a secret kind of knowing that I could always survive in the woods. Maybe this, more than anything else, is why I'm where I'm at at 50. I fit.

I guess the thing you got to ask yourself is, where do you fit? What is important to you? What feeds your soul? Living in the country does all of these things for me. Lord knows I'm getting rounder as I get older, so I must be well fed.

I don't have any pearls of wisdom to put down from Uncle Jack. He never really had any, more quiet than not; but he passed spirit to me. If I could put it in words, I would, but it's not something I can do. You either get it or you don't, kind of like getting the common sense or not. It's an either-or, kinda thing: either you got it or you don't. But you don't go find it. There isn't anything mystical happening out here in the country unless you already have the eyes to see it.

I put money down as one of my important rules, only because you need it. So let's talk about money. You just plain cannot live off the land. Trying to will cause untold amounts of heartaches between people. The issue is not so much the money, as the things money buys. So before you leave the city, start by discussing the things you're willing to do without because they cost money. And if you both agree on everything, you're not telling the truth.

What's not such a big deal when you're bringing in big bucks in the city can kill you on a limited income. That's why you need to practice homesteading in the place you're at before you ever move out to a remote area. Trust me on this. The hardest word you'll ever say to your beloved is "No." "Love" and "Yes" just seem to go together in this culture.

Well learning how to say "no" to each other's wants--not needs--is not fun, but it will save you a lot of grief later on down the road. You're going to be living a reduced standard of living out there. (Unless of course you've just sold that rancho in southern California and moved up here with us pee-ons. If that's the case, none of this will be pertinent to you anyway 'cause you likely don't have the eye yet.)

To the rest of you, get your steps ironed out and go for it. If you've done your homework, the hard work will fill your spirit, the remoteness your resources, the land your soul. It don't get any better than this. This I know, and I'm still hauling my own water, ten years now. I've hauled water longer than most homesteaders stay or most marriages last. I don't think of it as some kind of tribal passage in to the land of pure of spirit, I only point it out as sticking power.

When some night you have ventured far from home and hearth to go abroad visiting and you get hopelessly stuck five miles from home in below zero weather without any flashlight, believe me, you will need sticking power to make it home. It ain't the distance or the lack of a flashlight that will kill you, it will be one of you coming after the other with "Why did you bring me to this god-forsaken place?"

So practice before you leave the city so you can get that part out of the way before it happens. Because it will happen. Murph's law is perfectly intact out here in the hinterlands. Fact, in the wintertime, I think it's the law of the land. Cars will run perfectly fine all year long, until you really need 'em. Comes a cold front with two feet of snow just dumped on you, and the danged things develop into sculptures.

Speaking of getting dumped on, there's the other kind of dumped. Relationships. Let's see, in the ten years we been up here on the ridge, five couples out of seven have split from each other. Now I know lots of couples split up nowadays, but I think these odds are a little higher than the national average. This is a crow's fly survey of course, but I think it speaks of the heart of Rules 1-4. If you don't take care of the first 4, 5-7 will lead you to 8.

But my advice has been called into question more than once, so I'll just let it lay where it all fell. Works for me is all I can say. Individual differences become exaggerated in ways you'd never deem possible when you're confronted with adversities. Also, you will be confronted with situations you never had to deal with before in the city. I already mentioned water and electricity, but here are some other trials.

You buy your dream property, but fail to ask if it's buildable. Lots of states have zoning restrictions, yes, even out in the country. You need to ask about restrictions before you plunk down your hard-earned dollars. Don't bother asking the real estate agent or the person selling the property. Go straight to the government agency and find out. It can save you a lot of grief.

Check with the electric company in the area to find out how much it costs to run in power to a remote site. If it's prohibitive, you'll have to brew your own and I've already given you my opinion on that.

Does your property have a road that will be accessible in the winter? Will you have to have one put in? Bulldozing is an expensive proposition, 1/4 mile of road can run you $1000 easy. The farther you live from the resource center, call that the town, the more expensive it will be to get gravel hauled on your new road. You *will* need gravel. First real big stuff, then little stuff over the big stuff, so neither you nor your car die of displaced organs.

Okay now you're at the property. Did you build that designer playhouse? If not, building your dream house can easily turn in to a nightmare that will gobble every last soo you have. Minimum for about a 20 x 20 something with a country look (this means rustic) is about $5000 for a rough-framed, foil-finished interior (1990 prices).

Oh yes, you'll have to accomplish the road, the clearing for the homesite, the home, and cut a couple cords of wood so you'll be warm and cozy before the end of October. Snow is coming.

This brings us back to the driveway. The long, lovely, winding, private drive to the homesite is now a tortuous obstacle to access. You'll need a tractor to remove the snow. Hillside driveways can severely test your dry pants. Having no place to go, you can spend all day digging out just so you are secure in the knowledge that you can if you want to. Of course, if you need to work, it's a whole different ball game.

After a couple of months of the white stuff, you will encounter the thousand-yard stare. If you have children that you have to get to some remote bus stop, then your day will be already scheduled for you, with time for lunch in between going and coming to the bus stop. There are no latch-key kids out here, only jump-started parents.

Ah, the first melty days of spring come. Remember the driveway? If you shorted yourself by not putting rock on it, you'll be sorry. Also stuck. Did I forget to mention? White is not a country color, except for snow. Stick with various hues of brown: the mud doesn't show in the spring and the dust won't show in the summertime. Saves on the washing and on your appearance. It's hard to be "cool" in white when you're covered with various portions of the good earth.

Also, girls, no luxurious cremes and potions. After your trip to town you'll look like a wookie. If you think you can beat this by keeping the windows rolled up on a hot dusty day, you'll only end up looking like a wookie with streaks.

In the dry season, the yellow jackets will emerge. You'll have to plan all outdoor BBQ's early in the season. By August the yellow jackets give new meaning to the term flying food and they don't like to share.

By then, you'll know what time it is again. You'll have made it a year and it's time to fetch firewood. Time flies when you're having fun and before you know it, so also will the snow fly.

That's pretty much what it's about: each season comes and dictates the things you should be doing, then before you know it, it has passed, and another season, into another year. And there you have it.

. . . Elaine wouldn't have it any other way.

PR

Equipment

What Will You Need?

Well, what you will be doing when you get there? Will you be building your own house? Farming? Setting up a home business? Will you need snow removal equipment? Let's look at some of these topics and see just what the necessaries entail.

Some folks are disgusted at the thought of power tools, electric lights, and other trappings of civilization. Others won't do without them. You will have to decide that for yourself. "Homesteading" is not synonymous with "austerity." There is no conflict between homesteading and the utilization of technology. But if you think that you will be comfortable with kerosene lamps instead of electric lights, an axe instead of a chainsaw, and shovels instead of a tractor, be very objective in your thinking and don't neglect to try your new life style out in your pre-move year.

Distance

Purchasing most of your equipment, materials, and supplies during the year before your move to the woods presumes that you won't be moving across several states. Or an ocean. If your move is far enough that transporting all that stuff would be impractical, you'll probably have to settle for moving your tools, equipment and household goods and purchase your building materials closer to your new homesite.

There are exceptions to everything, and you really need to assess your own situation for the pros and cons of moving your stuff. For example, in some areas of the country, it is substantially cheaper to buy the entire package necessary to build a house elsewhere and have it shipped to your job site than to buy materials locally. Consider the local picture before you decide to do this, though. We have learned that the service we get from local suppliers is worth a great deal to us. That, together with our desire to help our local, independent businesses stay in business usually makes it worthwhile to do our buying at home.

If you do find yourself buying any equipment that must be shipped a significant distance, be sure to check various shipping options. As an example, when we had our diesel generator shipped from the Los Angeles area to Oregon, we discovered that the cost of shipping it the 1000 miles to Portland, our nearest "big" city, was about *one third* of the total cost of shipping it to our home, another eighty miles. The eighty-mile trip from Portland to our place, which was by way of a local freight line, would have cost twice as much as the 1000 mile trip with the cross-country freight line.

When you ask for freight quotes, ask for the rate both directly to your home, and the rate to your nearest major city. Of course, this assumes that whatever you're shipping is something you can haul the rest of the way in your own truck. A side-benefit to finishing the haul in your own truck is that it is often impossible to maneuver a big freight truck into just the right spot to off-load the equipment.

The smart move is to apply some of your pre-move year's research to determining the costs of the things you'll need both at your present location and your new one. By all means, don't let anybody talk you into garage-saling the tools and equipment you already own and replacing them after your move. It's always cheaper to move them than to replace them. See Chapter 6, "The Big Move."

Power tools in general:

If there is one rule here that is more important than any other, it is this: NEVER, EVER buy "homeowner" quality tools and expect them to do serious work. ALWAYS spend the extra few bucks for a professional-quality tool. Almost all power-tool manufacturers make two distinct lines of their products. One is designed for full-time use by professionals, and the other is designed for occasional, light-duty use by the average homeowner.

The safest route, if you are unsure about which line of tools is which, is to go to a dealer who supplies the wholesale and professional trades. If your budget suggests that you go for the cheaper tools, you are better off with a good, serviceable used professional tool than with a new consumer model.

The key here is what is called "duty cycle." The duty cycle of a tool is expressed in percentages. For example, if the duty cycle of a particular electric motor is 30%, that means that for any given amount of time that the motor is in service, it should be running only thirty percent of that time. In other words, for every three minutes you run the motor, you must let it cool off for seven minutes, or expect to smell smoke.

Not all tools have their duty cycles listed where the user can find them. Matter of fact, most don't list them at all, and if they do, it will be in the literature that was originally packed with the tool. But the point of this discussion is that most "consumer" grade tools are rarely rated at more than a 50% duty cycle. Some are as low as 20%. Most professional-quality tools are rated at a 100% duty cycle. That means they are designed to be operated at their full potential continuously. See the difference?

These same principles apply to gas-powered tools, as well. Weed-eaters, rototillers, and particularly chain saws, are all manufactured in both homeowner/consumer and professional models.

Back when we still used firewood, we used to go out to the woods with various friends and neighbors. We still have the same Stihl saw that we bought 20 years and over 100 cords of wood (mostly oak) ago. Most of our neighbors had shiny new saws recently purchased from various discount stores. Invariably, we ended up cutting both our loads of wood with our saw while our neighbor loaded both trucks. Either they couldn't get their toy saws started, or they'd break after a few minutes of operation.

Remember, your tools are vital to your survival. Buy tools intended for professional use. Most power-tool repair shops are good sources for used and/or reconditioned professional-quality tools of all types.

For specific-application tools, it is best if you can find a dealer who specializes in the particular trade in which the tool you seek is used. For example, if you're looking for a chainsaw, it is best to go to a logging-supply dealer. They don't often sell equipment that won't hold up in the field. (There is a reason why most timber-fallers don't shop for chainsaws at Sears or Walmart.) The logging-supply dealer's repair shop is also a good source for used or reconditioned saws. If the dealer doesn't do his own repairs, he can refer you to the shop that does.

Most power-tool repair shops are good sources for used and/or reconditioned professional-quality tools of all types.

Regarding warranty service on new tools, most warranty repairs can be handled by any factory-authorized repair shop. Buy your tools where you get the best price; warranty repairs are seldom required on professional-quality tools. We've been buying and operating professional-quality power tools for the last forty-odd years, and have never required a warranty repair. Even if you live hundreds of miles from the nearest service shop, UPS will be happy to transport your tools to and from the shop for you when a repair or some maintenance is finally necessary.

Buyer Beware

A phenomenon which has materialized in the last twenty-odd years is the local "discount" tool merchant. Sometimes he will publish a notice of an amazing sale in the newspaper, and rent a store for just this purpose. The sale is usually called a liquidation, or bankrupt stock sale or something along those lines. These vendors rarely have regular, permanent store locations; they're just around long enough for the sale.

One thing all of their merchandise has in common is that it is all made off-shore, and usually in China. Now, we're definitely not trying to knock Chinese manufacturing. Every manufacturing country makes good stuff and bad stuff, China included. But these tools are "real tool look-alikes." They are of such inferior quality that in most cases, you would be better off not having the tool at all than to think you had a tool to do the job only to find out that it will fail the first time you try to use it.

We've seen pipe wrenches that the teeth rounded off of on their first application to a pipe; open-end wrenches that fit so poorly they would just round over the corners of a nut rather than turn it. And if you find one that will actually grab the nut, the wrench will bend. Pliers in which the jaws don't line up, screw-drivers with tips so soft that they'll twist off on the first use. We could go on, but the point is: buyer beware! Again, you would be MUCH better off with old, used, even rusty, REAL tools from a garage sale than brand new, shiny, red, pretend tools. The pretend tools are attractively priced when compared to new real tools, but you can buy good, used tools more cheaply yet.

The exception to the above recommendations are tools that don't have moving parts, or in which the moving parts are not expected to be precision or hardened tool-steel. For example, an offshore anvil would be an OK tool: no moving parts. Some of the large bench-vises sold by these guys are OK and much cheaper than a name-brand similar tool. A vise has only a couple of moving parts, and for anything but the most strenuous (ab)use, if the look-alike vise works smoothly when new, it will probably be an OK tool.

The above cautions pertain to hand tools. There are several manufacturers and importers (whose own names appear on the tools they sell) of large power tools that are of excellent quality. These tools include drill presses, table saws, jointers, planers and such. The bottom line: be careful. Try before you buy. Get referrals.

If you know exactly what tool you're after (brand and model number), mail-order is a great resource. We've listed some of these businesses in our Resource Guide. Their prices are hard to beat anywhere, and at least one of them ships free in the continental US. There are others as well, and their full-page ads are carried in magazines having to do with construction, renovation and remodeling. Check your local library and compare prices. Don't forget to include freight when you figure costs; on heavy items such as some tools, freight charges sometimes can make a big difference.

What about 12-volt tools that will run on an alternative power system? Please read all about it in Chapter 11, Alternative Electrical Systems.

Building Your Own House

If you're planning to build your house from scratch, you probably already know what tools you will need. Your personal preferences will determine whether you use power tools or do everything by hand. If getting your house built in a timely fashion is important, power tools--at least the basic ones--may be a necessity.

Building your own home or doing an extensive remodel or up-grade involves a lot of careful planning. Part of that planning is to make sure you'll have the necessary tools on hand when you need them. Tools are expensive, so planning your tool needs during your pre-move year is essential.

The classifieds have turned up some incredible deals for us. So have garage sales, although garage sales can be frustrating because you may have to go to many for every one that yields a prize. Farm auctions are another excellent resource. Look for farm auctions in the newspapers of any farming-based community. Flyers posted in feed and tack stores, lumber yards, grocery stores and local bulletin boards are more sources. (Look under "auctions" in the resource guide for another good source of auctions and some sound advice on dealing with them.)

If you already are involved with carpentry, you probably already have everything you need. If not, some tools you may want to consider having on hand, in addition to those most commonly around, are a radial-arm saw and a set of wall jacks.

The radial-arm saw is invaluable for repetitive cuts of long, hard-to-handle framing members. When cutting dozens of long pieces that all have to be identical in length and/or angle of cut (like rafters), you load up the board (or several boards at a time, depending on the application), slide it to the preset stop on the table, and cut. No measuring each piece, and no chances for mis-measuring or mis-cutting.

Wall jacks, the kind that slide over a long 2 X 4, not only make singlehandedly lifting an entire wall a piece of cake, but they make wall-raising a safe and controlled operation.

Depending on the height of the house you plan to build, a good extension ladder is another great asset. And "good" means a top-rated, commercial-duty ladder. Stay away from consumer grade ladders, particularly long ones. They are flimsy and unsafe, and they are much more easily damaged than real ladders. Once the side-rail of a long ladder gets a kink in it, its structural integrity is gone.

How are you going to power those handy electric tools while building your house? Chapter 11, Alternative Electrical Systems, tells all about it.

Doing a job yourself that you would ordinarily hire out is a wonderful way of acquiring tools. For example, many years ago, we started pricing a whole kitchen full of cabinets for a house we were remodeling. After reviewing several quotations from cabinet shops, we tried pricing the job from a different angle. We found that we could buy a professional-quality 10" table saw, a router, jointer, bench-mounted belt sander and some assorted small tools, plus all of the materials and hardware--including an excellent book on the art of cabinet building--for less than the lowest quote for the finished job.

Over the years, we have acquired a lot of our more expensive tools by learning to do the job ourselves. We could then buy the tools and materials for less money than it would have cost to hire the job done. There are few things more satisfying than having done the job yourself--and having the tools available again for the next time.

We have applied this principal to larger concepts, as well. Chapter 6, The Big Move, tells how we did it with a moving van. We also did it with a D-4 dozer that became a handy tool for a homestead that got five feet of snow on its half mile of driveway.

Farming the Land

Farming, in this discussion, covers everything from a subsistence garden to a small produce-for-sale operation. The equipment you decide to use in your farming operation, like that for building your house, depends on how much you want to depend on power tools and/or fossil-fuel-burning tillers, tractors and such.

We advocate the slight compromises involved in the use of certain power equipment. For example, we think that a chainsaw that will cut a cord of firewood in exchange for a quart or so of gasoline is an acceptable compromise. Keeping a 5KW generator running all day long for the occasional use of a couple of small power tools is not.

Most small-engine powered tools fall into the category of acceptable compromises. Among these are rototillers, irrigation pumps, mowers and tractors. But let's qualify some of these.

Rototillers are like most other equipment: buy the consumer grade and you waste your money. The front-tined tillers available in hardware and department stores are just about useless on anything but little, tiny gardens of soft, fluffy soil. For a tiller to do any useful work, the tines must be behind the wheels. There are many brands of good, rear-tined tillers available, and some of the best ones are the oldest. Current marketing practices that demand that each new generation of a product be cheaper to manufacture, seldom yield a better product to the customer.

Watch the classifieds in several categories: farm equipment, equipment and machinery, auctions, estate sales, and even miscellaneous for sale. Check with farm-machinery dealers, too. They often take trade-ins on new equipment. And as with any piece of machinery, if you don't feel qualified to give the machine (and its accessories) a thorough evaluation, take along someone who does.

If you happen to come across a gas engine-powered machine that is being sold cheaply because of a tired or broken engine, remember that brand new small engines are fairly inexpensive. They range from about $130 for a 3.5 HP lawn-mower engine to around $950 for an industrial-quality 20 HP Kohler. Most of the 8-10 HP engines used on a lot of tillers run about $250-$400. (See Resource Guide.) It generaly doesn't pay to have any extensive repair work done to small gas engines. If the engine is tired enough to need serious repairs, replace it with a new one. That way, you also get a new carburetor, magneto, and all of the other parts that might be ready to expire in an old, repaired engine; not to mention a new-engine warranty.

Tractors

If you plan to work a garden of any size, a tractor might be in order. Tractors come in all sizes from "garden" models to huge. Best buys are most often found in the 20+ year-old small farm or orchard tractors, in brands like Case, Ford-Ferguson, and others. These rigs can be found for sale complete with lots of attachments, most of which will become indispensable at one time or another.

When we had our place on the mountain, we had a 1950 Case tractor that came with a hydraulic front-loader, a heavy-duty three-point-mounted grader blade, and a disc. That was one handy machine. We built a six-foot-wide snow plow blade that mounted on the loader mechanism, and it kept our driveway clear for years. The grader smoothed out our road after each spring thaw, and we used the disc to plow under the weeds every year on a large field that somehow never got planted.

The only drawback to our old tractor was that it did not have four-wheel-drive. We got it stuck lots of times, especially while plowing snow and grading muddy roads. Dependability was never an issue, though. When the thermometer dipped to ten below zero, not a rig on the place would start except the old faithful Case. The tractor always started, no matter what. Let's hear it for simplicity in engineering.

By the way, when the temperature gets below freezing, pulling the battery out of whatever rig you expect to start in the morning and storing it in the house, is good insurance. Lead-acid batteries operate at something like 25% of their normal capacity at ten degrees, and it gets worse as the temp drops. A super-cold engine is difficult to crank with the best of batteries, so it's asking an awful lot from your super-cold battery to do it. During those cold months, just take the couple of minutes to pull the battery and leave it in the house overnight. The battery will last a lot longer, too, if not subjected to the severe conditions imposed by super-cold starting.

Also in the good-buy category, even if more expensive, are the small Japanese tractors, like Yanmar and Kubota. Most of these units are diesels, which means that they are more fuel-efficient than gasoline-powered rigs. Parts are readily available, and these tractors are available in a wide range of sizes, many with four-wheel-drive. 4WD should be a serious consideration if you plan to use the machine on anything but nearly-level land, and especially for use in snow or anywhere near mud.

The small and medium-size Japanese tractors can be useful tools for anywhere up to a few acres of serious farming. Anything more than that, and you need to consider either a full-size farm tractor, or one of the large models of Japanese machines. A large Yanmar, Kubota or similar machine, especially with 4WD and a few accessories, is a serious working-machine.

A few points to inspect in your evaluations of used tractors: Be sure to check all of the hydraulic operations. Leave any hydraulic accessories extended for a few minutes to examine for leaks.

Also, diesel engines should start easily and not blow any visible smoke once warmed up to operating temperature. And contrary to what a lot of folks (especially those selling tractors) will tell you, it is not normal to have to use starting fluid to get a diesel engine running. Starting fluid is harmful to the engine because it washes the lubrication from the cylinder walls and causes a lot of unnecessary wear at start-up. You should be wary of any diesel engine that requires starting fluid to start.

Make sure that any tractor you are considering has a three-point hitch. These are the industry standard, and some older tractors didn't have them. The three-point hitch allows the use of rear-mounted implements that can be lifted hydraulically. On older units, check also for an operational power take-off (PTO). Check the Resource Guide for an excellent source for parts for ancient tractors.

In all cases, try to find a tractor with as many attachments as you can. It's always cheaper to buy the package now than to add the various implements later, when you find you need them. Bought as a package, everything will fit and work smoothly together, too. Often, a loader or other accessory bought after the fact will need modification to fit and operate correctly. Even if the implement fits, just having to buy a few hydraulic fittings can give your budget a real shock.

Snow-removal Equipment

During your planning-year, you found out what kind of snowfall you can expect, right? That information will determine what kind of equipment will be necessary to deal with it. First of all, just how much area will you need to clear of snow? Is your house (going to be) quite near the road, or will you have to clear a half-mile of driveway? Is your access road maintained, or will you be responsible for keeping a portion of it clear?

We kept our half-mile of road clear of snow with a blade built to mount on the loader mechanism of our old tractor. For a few of our years on the mountain, we had a Caterpillar D-4 dozer, which worked much better, especially in snow over three feet deep. When the time came that we no longer needed the dozer for anything but plowing snow, we sold it and reverted back to the old tractor. If other work on your homestead will require a lot of dozer use, it is well worth considering buying one rather than spending the same amount of money on hiring the work done.

On occasion, like when the county road crew was overloaded with work, we had to clear the four miles of secondary road between our place and the intersection with the main road. If we did it soon enough after a snowfall, and the snow was less than two feet deep, we used our home-made drag plow. A drag plow in its most primitive form is a railroad tie chained to the back of a four-wheel-drive vehicle in such a way that it stays crosswise to the road about fifteen feet behind the towing vehicle. A chain from each end of the tie to a trailer hitch works great.

We built a slightly more sophisticated plow out of plywood and lumber scraps and used it for years. It did an amazing job, too. Vehicle speed had to be maintained at about fifteen miles per hour, and at that speed, the plow threw snow twenty feet in both directions. Our road was quite rough, however, and the plow needed regular attention to keep it from coming apart. When we attached a piece of 1/2" plywood across the entire bottom of the plow, we virtually ended our maintenance problem.

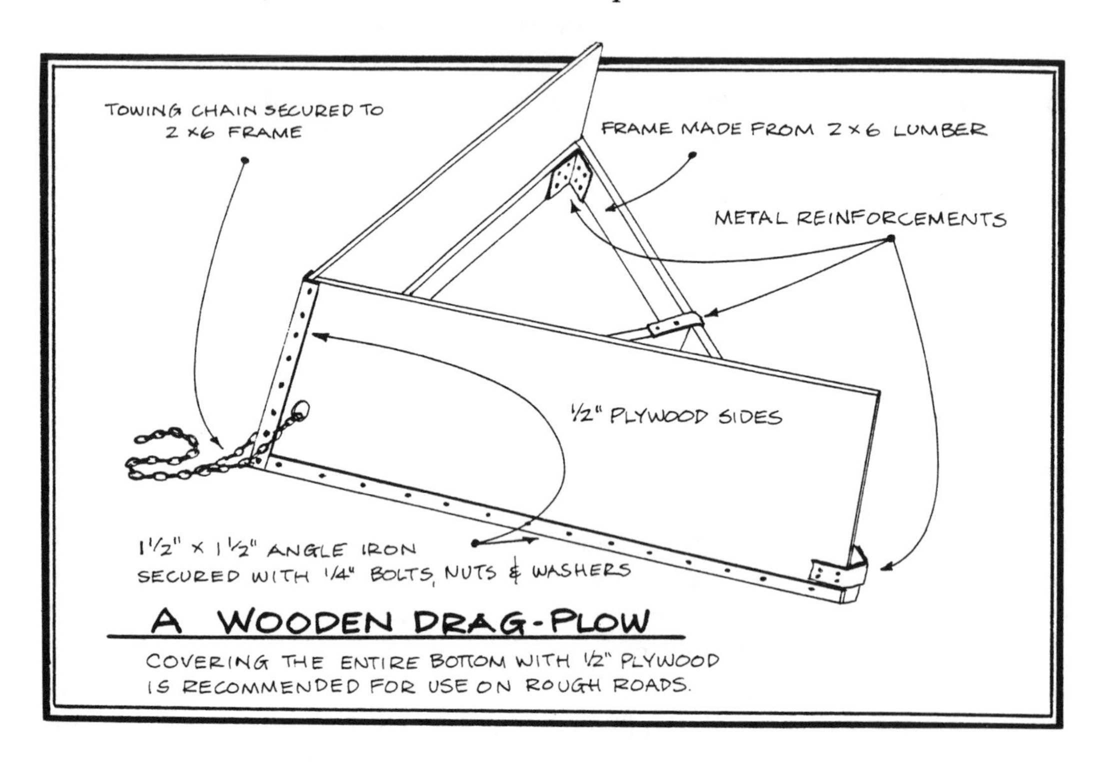

A WOODEN DRAG-PLOW

COVERING THE ENTIRE BOTTOM WITH 1/2" PLYWOOD IS RECOMMENDED FOR USE ON ROUGH ROADS.

The important details on a wooden drag plow are securing all critical joints with metal reinforcing brackets and straps, and making certain that the chain is attached directly to the framework, not just to the plywood. Assemble the unit with screws and bolts, not nails.

A chain works better than a rope for pulling the plow. Rope, being stretchy, allows the plow to hang up on tough spots and then bound ahead. A chain provides a constant pull and much better control. If you have the skills, materials, and the inclination, a welded steel framework is a better way to go.

A neighbor built his drag plow so that his kids could ride it as he cleared the road. And lest we be sued for suggesting that any parents subject their children to the inherent liability that such a possibly dangerous adventure might present, please be assured we're not. We're just telling you what our neighbors did. And how much fun they had.

Road Building and Land Clearing

Does your property need a substantial amount of dozer work? Clearing a building site and putting in a quarter-mile of road might not qualify as "substantial," but the size of the bids you get for doing the work may surprise you. Often, a good, serviceable dozer can be bought for not much more than the price of hiring your necessary work to be done.

Throughout this book, we recommend that you consider buying the tools to do the job yourself rather than to hire the job done, especially if the price comes out about the same. We have accumulated most of our tools and equipment over the years by this method, and we've gained a lot of new skills in the process. We're not suggesting that you always do every job yourself; you need to evaluate each situation as it come along. In some instances, the job at hand might be a once-in-a-lifetime thing, and the tools would rust away before you ever needed them again.

But more often than not, if the price comes out anywhere near the same, you're ahead to do it yourself. Buying your own dozer is worth considering if your place is large enough that you might eventually want to develop more of it, or maybe put in a pond. (Ponds require many hours of dozer work.) If you live in snow country, a dozer is a nearly unstoppable snow-removal machine.

Any time a bid on dozer work gets up into the $3000 to $4000 range, you can start dozer shopping. Caterpillar D-4 dozers in pretty good condition can be found in that price range. There are others around, too, but the Cats are easy to find new and used parts for, and they're good old machines. Don't despair if the one you find is forty years old. Properly maintained, it still has many years of life left in it.

It isn't difficult to learn to operate a dozer, either. It does take practice to get good with it, and it will surely take a novice a lot longer to do any given job than it would a professional operator, but so what? You'd be learning a new skill on your own piece of equipment that would not only serve your needs for years to come, but that could also be an income-producing tool, should you have the inclination.

Any dozer you want for all-around use has to have an angle blade. That means that the blade can be moved from straight across the machine to an angle to either side. This is most often accomplished by pulling out locking pins, swinging the blade to the new position, and re-inserting the pins. If you get real lucky, you can find a machine that has a hydraulic angle blade. Then you can move the angle to wherever you want it without getting out of the driver's seat.

If you are considering the purchase of a dozer or tractor and you aren't familiar with these machines yet, be sure to take along someone who is when you go shopping for one. There are some critical wear points that need to be inspected, and anyone familiar with heavy equipment will know exactly what to look for. Some of those "critical points" can get real pricey to repair, so a knowledgeable inspection is definitely in order. A good old dozer in serviceable condition, however, can do the modest amounts of work demanded by most homesteading situations for many years with no more expense than routine maintenance.

In the next chapter, Vehicles, we discuss the merits of utility trailers used in conjunction with the family car for hauling building materials. That discussion also covers what to look for in the selection of a trailer, and where to find them.

The same utility trailer you use with your car or truck can also be very useful behind a tractor. We put a lot of miles on our trailer out in the woods behind the tractor bringing in firewood and moving pumps and equipment, fence posts and wire, you name it. A simple drawbar hitch is easily installed on almost any tractor.

The equipment needs for hauling your water and generating your own electricity are covered in Chapters 11, 12, and 13.

Before you finalize your decisions about what you'll need, especially if you think you can get by with very little, visualize yourself in your new lifestyle a few years down the road. You might be very happy living a life that is as simple and basic as camping, for a while. But when the novelty wears off, you may find it extremely difficult to make an adjustment back to a more contemporary lifestyle unless you have set aside funds for just that eventuality. Again, testing your new lifestyle in the year before you move is the best practice you can get.

BEAST

Vehicles

In General...

One more element of independence is transportation. Will you need four-wheel-drive in the winter and during the spring thaw? Will you need a heavy-duty pickup? An economy car for passenger trips to town and elsewhere? We heartily recommend two vehicles if at all possible.

Heavy-duty pickups and trucks or vans can be expensive to operate. They gump indecent amounts of fuel, and have big, expensive tires that wear out fast if used for daily transportation. If you need an occasional truck and you also have an efficient, small car, you can save the truck for when you need its utility.

Another real bonus of having two vehicles is that if one becomes inoperable for any reason, you have the other as a backup. This becomes more important in a direct ratio to your distance from town.

Insurance

One significant expense associated with vehicle-ownership is insurance. Insurance rates vary a great deal between states, so if you are not already familiar with the rates in the area in which you intend to reside, you might want to check before you run out and acquire that second vehicle.

To most of us, insurance is a four-letter word. We all hate the thought of it, and our family certainly doesn't have what most insurance sellers would consider enough. But it is not in keeping with an attitude of self-reliance and peace toward our fellow earth-inhabitants to drive a vehicle and not carry liability insurance.

How would it affect your family if someone caused an accident that ended up costing thousands of dollars in hospital bills? What if that accident did nothing more than total your vehicle, and that person just shrugged his shoulders and said, "Sorry about that, but I don't have any insurance...or any money"? Assuming a decent driving record, the cost for liability coverage is at a minimum for those of us who live in the boonies and don't drive much. Don't drive away without it.

One Rig or Two?

If you find that insuring two vehicles is more than your budget can handle, you'll need to decide on a combination (read: compromise) rig to handle all your requirements.

For example, if there are only two of you, and you only occasionally need to haul oversize loads (like long planks or other building materials), a small pickup with a lumber rack might do the trick. If you need to haul heavy and/or large loads a lot, you'll need a full-sized pickup. Again, a well-designed lumber rack is an indispensable asset.

We've seen lots of racks that would qualify as "well designed," except for one thing. Very few have a removable back-bar. The piece of metal that goes across the back is usually welded in place, making the loading of large, bulky objects difficult at best. It's easy to make that back-bar either swing out of the way or just lift off the rack, and that little feature can double the utility of any rack.

When we were still on the Oregon coast, our family's needs were in the "heavy-and/or large loads" category, but we lived in rain country. A full-size van worked best for us. Ours was an 18 year-old, long-wheelbase Chevy in good shape, and it had an easily-removable back seat, increasing its versatility even more. With the back seat removed, 4x8 foot sheets of whatever fit with room to spare.

Full-size vans and trucks burn about twice as much gas per mile as do the smaller rigs, but you can buy a lot of gas for the price of some annual insurance premiums, not to mention all the other expenses of owning that second vehicle. You'll have to make these decisions based on the amount of driving you will be doing (and how much time you like to spend servicing and repairing vehicles). The other consideration involves how far you live from town and how valuable the distance involved makes having a backup vehicle.

Another cost consideration is getting supplies to your homestead, particularly if you're building. It doesn't take too many delivery charges from lumber yards to pay the annual expenses of running your own vehicle. If staying within budget is important to you, do the research and put the numbers on paper.

Tires

A fairly big expense item is tires. New tires have become very expensive, and there are ways to get the most miles-per-dollar from your tires. One trick we've been using for years is to buy "new car take-offs" from tire dealers. More than a few people who buy a brand-new car take it right to the tire shop to replace those "wimpy" factory tires with something more macho or flashy. The tire shop takes the new ones in on trade, and since they do have some miles on them and aren't technically new, they sell them at about half the price of new ones.

Another excellent source of good used tires is the auto dismantler (formerly known as a wrecking yard). Dismantlers buy hundreds of cars from insurance salvage pools, and lots of them have nearly-new tires on them. Your local dismantler is a good place to get premium tires at half the price of bargain-basement ones. Put tires on your shopping list the next time you head for the big city, where there are more salvage yards. You never really need to buy *new* tires.

You can also save money on tires by buying the premium quality model. Premium tires outlast the cheapos by a wide margin--particularly truck tires. We used to wear out a set of recapped snow tires on our truck every winter. When we switched to a set of used high-dollar name-brand snow tires, we ran the same tires for four winters and they were still in good shape when we sold the rig with the homestead. We're not trying to talk you into shopping for the most expensive tires you can find; just don't let the cheapest price be the only deciding factor. Used premium tires are generally a better buy than new bargain tires.

Last but not least, if you need aggressive snow treads to get you through the winter, by all means invest in an extra set of wheels so that you can have your summer and winter tires mounted permanently. Having to switch and re-balance tires on a single set of rims every season is an expensive, time-consuming nuisance. But with an extra set of wheels you need only to switch wheels in the spring to get back on highway tires. And if you do switch back to your highway tires as soon as is practical, you can use your killer, studded snow tires for many winters; for deep-lugged, all-terrain tires wear out at an alarming rate on pavement.

Car and Trailer

There is another alternative to operating two vehicles. If your needs are mostly the transportation of people and small goods, but you occasionally need to haul large or heavy objects, a mid- to full-size car and a utility trailer stout enough to move your anticipated loads would serve you nicely. Trailers are generally cheap to license (some states don't even require that you register trailers) and generally require no additional insurance policy. (Check your policy to see that it covers the hauling of a utility trailer. Most do.)

The reason for the mid- to full-size car is that it is dangerous to haul a load (combined weight of trailer and its load) that weighs more than the towing vehicle. Also, most compacts are light-duty vehicles without brakes that are capable of safe operation with the added weight of a trailer. Nor are their engines or transmissions usually up to the task.

If you opt to go for the car/trailer combination, be sure to install a permanent, heavy-duty, frame-mounted hitch that is rated for at least the combined weight of the trailer and the heaviest load you might ever place on it.

Utility trailers are available from several sources. They often appear in newspaper classified ads, and yellow pages "trailer" listings will direct you to manufacturers and dealers. Before our move to Hawai'i, we had a trailer built by a custom shop in Portland, Oregon. We found that having one built was cheaper than buying any of the used rigs we could find.

Be wary of homebuilt trailers; if you are unsure of the quality of the welding and general construction of a prospective trailer, have it checked by a welding shop.

A utility trailer needn't be fancy, but it does have to have legal tail and stop lights and a safety chain; and it should have tie-down hooks down both sides, and stake-pockets all around for the installation of side-racks. If you will be hauling building-materials-sized loads on your trailer, find one that has full-sized car wheels and tires.

Stay away from the light-duty and/or collapsible trailers altogether. An alternate to the stake-pockets and tie-downs is a trailer with permanently-installed side- and front-walls, and a tailgate. We feel that for maximum versatility, the flat-bed trailer works better. Matter of fact, we have yet to install the side-boards on our trailer, and we've hauled a lot of materials on it. The flat-bed configuration is easier to load and unload, and it allows you to place long loads out over the tongue of the trailer. Just today, we hauled a neighbor's pool table, a task that would have been impossible had the trailer been built with permanent sides. And at the lumber yard, a flat-bed trailer can be loaded directly with a forklift, something you can't do with either a side-board trailer or a pickup.

As mentioned in the previous chapter, another use of a utility trailer on the homestead is in conjunction with your tractor.

All things considered, if you can handle the extra expense, the added utility and the backup value of a second vehicle are certainly worth consideration. Particularly the backup value. It's no fun being stuck umpteen miles from town with a broken rig and no way to get parts.

Optional Extras

While we're at it, let's talk about automotive optional equipment. There are those who will tell you that you should never buy a car with power-anything, because "all those needless gadgets are just more things to fix." In all of our years in the auto business, we saw so few failures of *any* power equipment that we heartily recommend that you avail yourself of any that suits your needs.

If you will be living where there are weather extremes, particularly those which include hot, dusty summers, by all means go for air conditioning. When we lived up on our mountain, there were eight miles of thick, dry dust between us and the closest pavement. With no AC, the dust would get into the car even if you could stand to have the windows up. With them down, you would simply be caked with sweat-soaked dust by the time you got to town. The whole inside of the car was covered with dust. Dust eventually filled the speedometer and all the other gauges, but not until long after it had destroyed the cassette player and the radio.

After we got a car with air, we left the windows up and switched the AC controls to "max," which recirculated the air in the car rather than bringing in more dust-laden air from outside. What a change! We could actually arrive in town ready to do business without needing to bathe first.

During the winter months, or during any kind of weather when the windows get fogged up on the inside, running the AC with the heater controls set to "warm" defrosts the windows instantly and keeps them that way. This is a little-known use for air-conditioning, and we consider it a terrific safety feature.

Power steering and brakes have become so standardized that it's hard to find a rig without them any more. Power steering is a valuable asset in any vehicle that is to be operated on rough roads. This is especially true with pickups and 4WD vehicles. Without power steering, running a tire up against a rock or a deep rut can literally yank the steering wheel right out of your hand. Not so with power steering.

For an in-depth discussion on power accessories and all other areas of getting the most miles per *dollar* out of any vehicle, we recommend reading *Games Dealers Play, the Complete Car Book.* (See the Resource Guide.)

Four Wheel Drive?

Regarding four-wheel drive, if you won't need it, don't bother. All other things being equal, a 4WD vehicle won't go as far on a gallon of gas, it has an extra differential and the associated machinery to maintain (and wear out), and 4WD's always cost more to begin with. If you will be operating both a car and a truck, and you will need 4WD occasionally but rarely, buy a 4WD truck and use it when you really need the extra traction. Or better yet, just chain up your two-wheel drive rig on the few days you need to. In areas where a standard rear-wheel-drive car would have trouble maintaining traction, a front-wheel drive rig can be an inexpensive compromise. A front-wheel drive car will go places where a rear-wheel drive would be totally helpless.

Is Newer Better?

Should you spend money on a fairly new car or truck? Only if you have money to burn. If you can find one, a well-maintained older rig is always a better deal. The newer the car (or truck), the more electronic computer-controlled gadgets have been installed to keep you or even a non-factory-franchised mechanic from being able to service it. The best bet is the freshest, well-maintained fifteen- to twenty-year old vehicle you can find. Or even older. Most of these older rigs, if they're still in good condition now, will be on the road long after the delicate, temperamental plastic imports of today have been recycled. (And "imports" includes a lot of so-called domestic vehicles, since most of their parts are made off-shore.)

Today's cars are, for the most part, very dependable. Right up until they get old enough or accumulate enough miles for problems to start. That's when you discover that repairs start costing as much as the car is worth . . .if you can find someone to do the repairs. All newer cars are laden with dealer-access-only computer hardware. Only the dealer with his dedicated diagnostic equipment can service these cars. And the dealer can (and usually does) charge what the market will bear.

Gone are the days of being able to repair a car on the spot. New cars automatically get towed to the dealer's garage for any kind of breakdown, because the standard repair procedure is to simply replace whichever electronic module failed this time. And the only way to determine which module failed is with the dealer's specialized diagnostic equipment. Funny how our older cars used to run forever without all that electronic stuff....

The farther you are from town, the more important it becomes that you be able to service/repair your vehicles where you are and with what's available. And that pretty much lets out most vehicles built since the early eighties.

Evaluate your needs carefully, and plan your equipment accordingly.

Maintenance

One of the most important maintenance items for any internal combustion engine is the regular oil change. Regular oil changes can easily double the life of an engine over one where oil is merely added when low. "Regular" means no longer than 3000 miles or three months (which ever comes first) between changes.

It is also important to use the correct oil for the application. Any major-brand, top-of-the-line oil is fine for gas-engine vehicles. Diesels, because of their much higher combustion pressures, require an oil specifically marked for diesel service.

If you drive a lot of dusty roads, oil needs to be changed even more frequently. Air-cleaner elements need more frequent attention in dusty service, too. Replace any air-cleaner element that is covered with a fine layer of dust. Inspect the inside of the air-cleaner housing to make sure that dirt is not leaking past the element. Keep the inside of the housing clean. It takes very little abrasive dust to destroy an engine quickly.

The value of adequate preventive maintenance cannot be overstressed. Preventive maintenance becomes even more important the farther you live from the nearest repair facility or parts source. Just about every instance of a vehicle failure that we have ever witnessed in our neighbors' vehicles (and they were many) was a direct result of the lack of preventive maintenance. Contrary to popular opinion, BREAKDOWNS ARE *NOT* A FACT OF LIFE.

When you first buy a used vehicle, check it over very carefully from one end to the other. *Games Dealers Play* (see Resource Guide) has a thorough rundown on checking out cars and trucks. If you don't feel qualified to check it out yourself, have a competent mechanic do it this time. But by all means, if you are about to embark on an adventure in homesteading, being able to fix and service your vehicles is right up near the top on your list of essential skills. If you have to have someone else work on your car or truck for the time being, watch and/or work with that person. Get a service manual for the vehicle (available at most parts stores) and get familiar with how the rig works and how to take care of the normal service procedures.

If you always see to it that your vehicle is in good repair and is equal to the tasks you will demand of it, you will always be able to depend on it. That means that when you hear a funny noise, listen up: the car is trying to tell you something. Don't ignore it and hope it will go away. Strange noises are often the beginning of a mechanical problem that, if caught immediately, can be as simple as tightening a loose bolt; but if ignored can turn into a serious and costly breakdown. There is nothing mysterious about a vehicle; it is a simply a piece of machinery. All machines require periodic inspections, corrections, and maintenance if they are to keep running at top performance.

Happy motoring.

Getting the Most out of Your Wood Stove

A Stove by Any Name...

If you are moving to where it gets cold, when winter comes will your wood stove be all ready to go? Is it efficient enough to meet your own and the EPA's requirements? Or will you be ready to make the investment that the purchase and installation of new heating stoves has become?

There are dozens of snazzy new stoves on the market, both with and without the catalytic converters which are required by law in some areas. All new stoves are very expensive. Some don't even need firewood.

Pellet stoves seem at first glance to be an environmentalist's dream: they efficiently burn pellets made from recycled wood-processing byproducts. If this strikes your fancy, you should also, as they say, read the fine print.

First, check in your area for the availability and price of pellets. They aren't cheap. Then realize that these stoves require full-time 110-volt electricity to operate. When the power shuts down, so does your stove; not a comforting thought. That means that if you're buying public power and there's a power failure in the middle of winter (when they usually happen, especially in rural areas), you better have another source of heat for your home.

If you generate your own power and plan to install a pellet stove, you will need to figure its constant drain into your system requirements. The bottom line is that to be objective, you need to add up the costs of not only the stove, but also of the electricity to run it and the pellets and the fuel required to go get them, when making your comparisons to the cost of operating a conventional wood-burning stove.

Making the Best of What You've Got

If you are not eager to invest a small fortune in a new heat stove, you still have viable alternatives: make your existing stove perform better or replace it with another second-hand one which will. You say your budget precludes spending over a thousand dollars for a new stove? Here are a few tricks that will make most old stoves perform better than when they were new by getting them to produce more heat and hold a fire better, and/or by improving airflow in the building to eliminate hot and cold spots.

Improving the performance of the stove itself can be as simple as replacing a leaky door-gasket on an airtight model or as involved as completely rebuilding a drafty antique.

In seeking optimum performance from fabricated steel airtights like Earth Stoves or Blaze-Kings, first replace any frayed or missing door gaskets. These seals are made of fiberglass and they do wear out and get damaged by careless wood handling.

If the stove has a thermostat, make sure that it operates freely and that its draft-door closes tightly. If possible, observe the action of the draft-door as the stove heats up. The draft should be wide open when the stove is cold and should slowly close as it comes up to its normal operating temperature.

Check welds for cracks, especially if there is evidence that the stove has been overheated. Even a small crack can admit enough air to seriously alter the performance of the stove. Air leaks can often be detected by moving a burning stick of incense around any suspect areas when the stove is in operation. The smoke trail will lead you to the leak.

Modern cast-iron stoves like those from Vermont Castings, Waterford, and others, can develop leaks where the various cast pieces are joined. These joints are carefully sealed at the factory. But after years of heating/cooling cycles, even moving the stove carefully can affect the integrity of these seals.

Antique stoves, even those which produce lots of heat, are generally considered more decorative than functional because their abundant air leaks result in high fuel consumption and the need for constant refueling. Improving the performance of drafty antique stoves presents a whole new challenge.

Don't be too concerned if the door on your antique doesn't have an absolutely airtight seal. Every stove needs some air if it's going to support a fire. If the rest of the stove is made airtight, the draft can be adjusted to compensate.

Most cast iron stoves, like the box or parlor models, can be significantly improved by simply sealing all of the joints. Stove cement, available at your nearest hardware store or stove dealer, comes in tubes which fit into an ordinary caulking gun.

Antique wood-fired ranges, because of their many openings which admit air to the firebox, just can't be made air-tight. However, because of their large radiating surfaces and mass, they can be efficient heaters as well as wonderful ranges.

Cook stoves generally have tiny fireboxes, and the way to best efficiency is to keep a floor of ash on the grates to minimize the airflow, and maintain a constant hardwood fire. A chunk or two of coal at bedtime will keep the stove warm all night. Coal must be placed in the middle of the firebox and on a bed of ash.

> Note: *Coal burns at a high enough temperature to destroy castings on a wood stove--or even burn right through a tin stove. Never pile coal on the grates or against the sides of a firebox which was not specifically built for coal.*

Antique stoves which have a thin, sheet-metal liner supported by cast-iron end plates will usually need to have the liner replaced. Disassemble the stove and keep the old liner as a pattern from which to make the new one. If the construction of the stove allows for a heavier liner, have your sheet-metal shop make the new one of 18-gauge (or the heaviest gauge that will work) steel. When you reassemble the stove, make sure to seal the connection between the liner and both end plates with stove cement.

When disassembling an old stove, an easy way to remove rusted nuts from their respective bolts is to tighten them until they break. It's surprising how easily a rusted screw will break when tightened.

Never use a hammer on cast-iron; the stuff is unbelievably fragile.

Another trick to loosen badly rusted parts is to apply heat. Heat the rusted part until it glows red for a moment, let it cool, and remove it with normal tools. (This trick is for use on stoves. Don't use heat to remove rusted hardware on anything that you are unsure of. Excessive heat can dangerously alter the temper of steel.)

When re-assembling the stove, always use new nuts and bolts. When assembling parts which need to be removed for periodic cleaning and maintenance, use stainless nuts and bolts, available at most hardware stores and lumber yards. They cost more, but for the few that you will be using, the price difference is insignificant. And when you have to remove them, you will appreciate the small investment.

Any heating stove should be no larger than necessary. A huge stove in a small space will often be operating in its cool temperature range, and that assures a rapid buildup of dangerous chimney deposits.

Note: *Never use galvanized metal on stove parts! The fumes produced by the heated zinc plating are lethal.*

Of all the stoves we ever used, our all-time favorite was a circulator sold by Montgomery Ward in the thirties. Before finding this treasure on a neighbor's trash pile, we used a Scandinavian Jotul to heat our then-1000 square-foot home. The Jotul was a real fuel-miser and produced an incredible amount of heat, but we had to overheat the room in which it sat to get any warmth to the rest of the house. The Jotul, as are all stoves designed to produce heat off every surface, was a "radiator." What we needed was a "circulator."

A circulator need not be an antique; several are in current production. A circulator encloses a radiator in a metal box that allows airspace all around the stove and is open at the top and bottom. The air between the stove and the outer box heats quickly and rises out of the top opening as cold air from the floor enters the bottom opening to get heated, and so on.

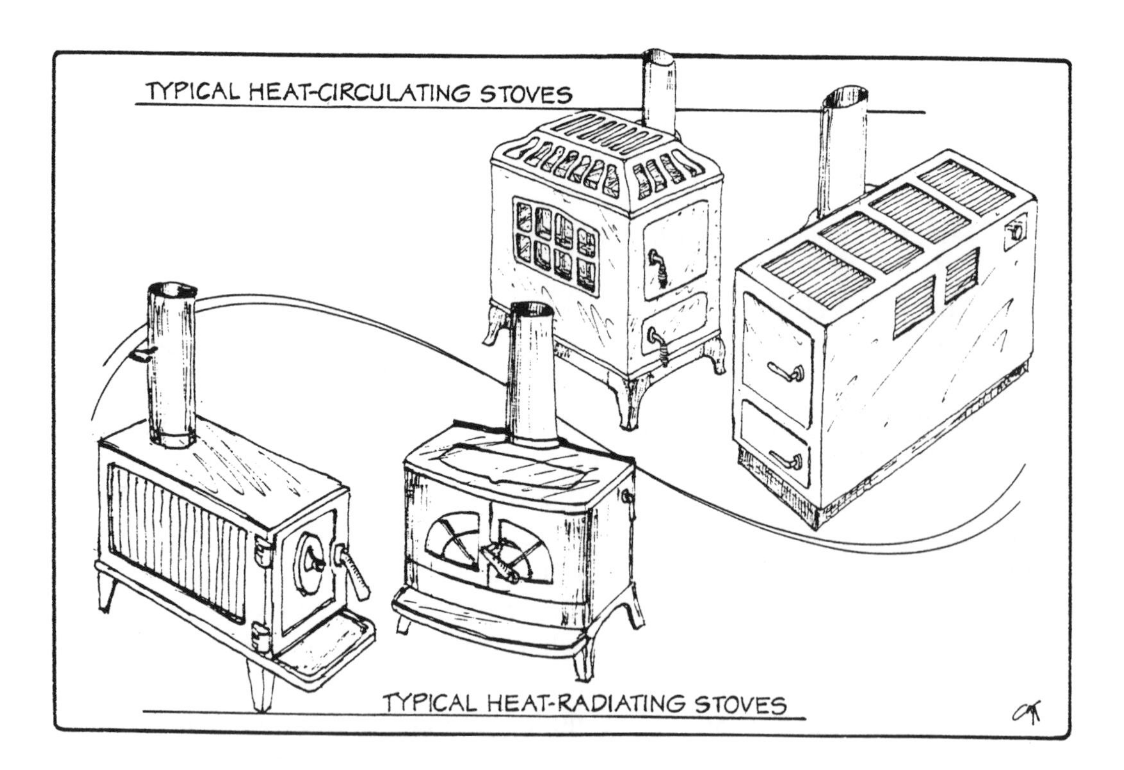

The cooler temperature of the outer jacket of a circulating stove is a distinct advantage if you have small children. An accidental bump into the stove will be uncomfortable, but it will not result in injury.

The Montgomery Ward stove had been discarded because its thin, sheet-metal walls had burned and rusted through making it both a smoker and a very real fire hazard. The top and bottom of the firebox were heavy cast iron, and the liner was an oval cylinder of sheet metal between them. (See drawing, page 181.) A sheet metal shop made us a new liner out of 18 gauge black iron, which was much heavier than the original liner.

This heater made an amazing difference in warming our home. Instead of cooking us out of one room and leaving the rest of the house cold, the heat, which now poured from the top of the stove, created a convective loop which warmed the whole house to nearly the same temperature. The outer jacket got hot, but not so hot that you couldn't touch it. (It had the cutest little butt-print on one side from where four-year-old Jake backed up against it in his new, fuzzy pajamas. The PJ's left the print; his behind was unscathed.)

Chimney cleaning

Always make certain that your chimney is clean. Chimney fires burn down a lot of homes every year, and they are entirely avoidable. For the first season that you are using your new stove (even if it's only new to you), climb up on the roof and check the chimney at least once a month. You may not have to clean it each time, but you will get an idea of how fast the creosote and soot are building up. Once you know what to expect, you can adjust your cleanings accordingly.

Burning only dry wood is one way to keep chimney buildups to a minimum. Wet or green wood and slow-burning fires will ensure rapid buildups. Stuffing your stove full of green wood and banking it down for the night is the surest cause for the most buildup.

We figured out a system that kept our double-wall chimney-pipe clean indefinitely. First, we kept our 24-hour-a-day stove fueled with dry wood. At night, we loaded it to the top and banked it for the night. Then in the morning, we would tap down the pile of hot, glowing coals, and fill the stove with dry kindling. The resulting very hot fire would create an instant mini-chimney-fire that would turn the night's accumulation of chimney-crud into a fine dust. After we heard the dust tinkling down the chimney, we would fill the stove with its first load of real wood for the day.

Safety First

Make sure your stove has a fireproof pad under it and that the pad extends out far enough to catch any embers that might pop or fall out while refueling. We've seen an awful lot of close calls from undetected embers catching a floor or rug on fire.

Another safety tip: although this might seem fairly obvious, apparently it isn't, because we've seen several fires as a result of people emptying ashes from their stoves into a bucket and then placing the bucket outside on a wooden floor. Most of the problems happened when the stove had been out long enough for the owner to assume that the ashes were cold. Don't bet the farm on cold ashes. Either dump the ashes in a safe place immediately, or place the bucket outside on dirt and away from anything combustible.

Moving the Heated Air

Once your stove is operating at peak efficiency, how do you get the heat where it's needed?

Ceiling fans are a cost-effective way to reduce fuel bills and even out temperatures. When we installed a ceiling fan near our circulating stove, the temperature evened out even better. We also cut way down on wood consumption. The stove did a better job of heating the house evenly, and did it with a smaller fire.

If your home has high ceilings or an open loft, most of the heat rises to those areas and eventually migrates out through the roof. A well-placed fan will move this stratified hot air down to your living spaces, as well as lowering the upstairs temperatures.

If your home has a forced-air furnace in addition to a wood stove, you have a wonderful opportunity to even out temperatures and to keep heated air from collecting high in the building. Most furnaces (gas, oil or electric), have a "summer switch," which allows the blower to run without having the furnace heat on.

Install an air duct at the highest point in the house, and route this duct into the cold-air return of the furnace. Then when your woodstove is running, and the heated air starts to collect up there near the ceiling, the fan in your furnace (with the heating part of the furnace turned off) will pull the warm air down the new duct and distribute it throughout the house.

You can also use a variation of this trick even if you don't have a forced-air furnace. If you have some problem cold-spots in your home that just never seem to get any of the heat from your stove, build the same kind of air-duct as in the example above, and with a large, slow-running (read: quiet-running) squirrel-cage blower, direct the otherwise-wasted warm air into the cold spots.

A good source for used squirrel-cage blowers, complete with housings and even some duct-work, is your local furnace/sheet-metal/heating installer. When a burned-out furnace is replaced with a new one, the blower and motor are usually still in fine working shape. Look in the yellow pages.

And finally, here's a neat trick we learned by accident. Ever light your cold stove only to have it start pouring smoke into the room? Try this: open the nearest exterior door of your house. The incoming rush of air will reverse the airflow in the stove. You need leave the door open only as long as it takes for the chimney to draw, usually a few seconds. It's like magic!

Much of the charm of a wood stove is magical, and if it's running at peak efficiency, its enchantment will endure.

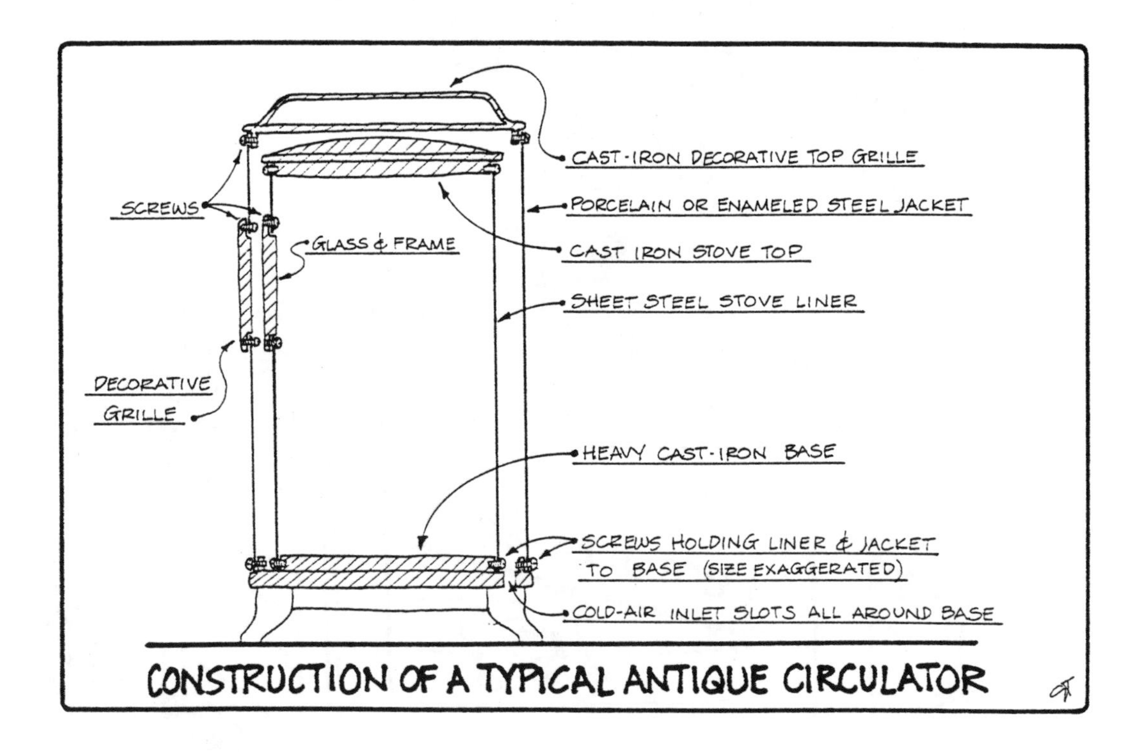

CONSTRUCTION OF A TYPICAL ANTIQUE CIRCULATOR

Lemonade
5¢
S.C.

Earning Your Keep at Home

Where to Begin

We have already established that it is nearly impossible to run a homestead without a dependable source of income. (There is a discussion about retirement income in Chapter 3, Money Matters.) But what if you still need to earn your beans and bacon? Ideally, wouldn't you like to earn that income right at home? Not only would you enhance your feelings of independence and self-sufficiency, but you could enjoy another level of togetherness with your family.

We've seen a lot of folks pack it in and head back to town because they "couldn't find a job." It seems somehow foolhardy to set off on a homesteading adventure when the whole show is dependent on finding a job in the nearest town. Especially when most small towns have one thing in common: significant unemployment. When a job does come up, it's much more likely that it will go to a local than to a newcomer.

It has always been our feeling that anyone who can do anything well, can find work just about anywhere. That's work; not necessarily a job. Let's face it, if you've got what it takes to be a successful homesteader (and we hope we have not been remiss in pointing out what it takes), then you've also got what it takes to be in business for yourself. You may well need some *work* to generate an income, but you do not need a *job*.

If it just happens that a job works out for you, that's great. But remember: any time you are working for someone else, your employer has to make a profit from your efforts if he's going to stay in business. If you are in business for yourself, your earnings (assuming you run your business in a businesslike manner) reflect the wage *and* the profit, not just the wage.

The number of people running successful home businesses is amazing. More and more folks living in homestead situations are happily earning their keep at home. Some are just getting by, and others are earning as much or more than they did at straight jobs in the city. And all of them are having more fun than they would be if they were working for someone else.

There are lots of publications available addressing the work-at-home concept. Basically, most business fall into either of two categories: service- or product-oriented businesses. When you narrow down the choices to a few different areas, check at your local library for both books and magazines addressing the work-at-home side of each field. Here is a broad view of some endeavors that lend themselves to home-business:

- Desktop publishing
  - newsletter
    - specific topic
    - general interest
    - local home-school
  - local jobs
    - letterheads
    - business cards
    - menus
    - forms
    - flyers
    - sales brochures
  - self-publishing
    - books, your own or others'
    - booklets
      - tourist information
      - recipes
      - how-to's
      - local history/culture
    - newspapers
      - arts/music/happenings coverage
      - tourist information
      - political forum
      - local news/events
      - all of the above

- Repair business
  - farm machinery
  - auto/light truck
  - computers
  - home electronics
  - appliances
  - home-handyman stuff
  - any combination of the above

Strange to recommend computers/home electronics for a wilderness-home-based business? Word travels swiftly in the country. If you are good at something and charge reasonable rates, you will be surprised how many computers and related peripherals (for example) will appear out of nowhere.

Carpentry-related
- framing
- complete building contracting
- concrete
- roofing
- remodeling
- painting

These aren't exactly "home" businesses, inasmuch as you won't be able to build someone their home at yours. The business is, however, run from your home; you decide the hours that you work, and you call the shots.

Welding
- at home in your shop
  - repairs
  - fabricating equipment and related products
- with portable truck-mounted welder
  - on-site repairs at neighboring ranches/farms
  - heavy machinery at job site

We've seen "have welder-will travel" welders keep real busy in the country.

Manufacturing (for the welder)
- truck racks, utility trailers and related equipment, can be custom/made-to-order or made-up-for-inventory and perhaps sold through a dealer in town

Furniture
- sold through a dealer in town, an artist's co-op, or at your home-studio, if you are anywhere near a tourist area or even a good-sized city

Various fine-arts or crafts goods
    Sold through nearby artist's co-ops, galleries, stores,
    or at various fairs and events (if you're willing to travel)

Sewing
    alterations and repairs
    manufacture of sewn goods, fabric or leather

We had a neighbor who made custom-designed, belt-hung "holsters" for equipment used by surveying crews. She researched the market and found a need to fill.

Bookkeeping
    personal tax returns
    business accounting

Many other business needs can be taken care of by modem on your home computer, too.

Computer-based businesses
    setup, configuring, maintenance and repair
    training others to use their computers (classes or one-on-one)
    programming (work at home for a distant company)
    Internet-based businesses (see end of this chapter)

These include working with a business in town (any town, anywhere) doing exactly what you would be doing if you were there, only doing it at home via modem. It is surprising how many computers there are around, and how few of them are used to their potential. There is a need almost everywhere for help in setting up programs and peripherals, teaching people how to run them, and just showing folks (including business folks) how to get the most out of their equipment. Magazines like Home Office Computing are valuable resources for home-business opportunities.

Heavy equipment operator

In several areas of this book, we recommend that if you need a job done, and find that you can buy the equipment to do it yourself for anywhere near the same price as having the job done, by all means, buy the equipment. This applies well to machines like dozers and tractors. Owning a dozer (and knowing how to operate it well) gives you an instant business opportunity. There is almost always someone nearby who needs some dozer work done, and the going rate in most areas of the country is around $30/hour for a small machine. (See Chapter 15, Equipment.)

Tractor work

- grading
- plowing
- disking
- mowing
- anything else your machine is equipped to handle

There are folks around who would love to plant that certain several acres every year if they could find someone reasonable to do the machine work. These are the people who don't have quite enough tractor work around to justify buying their own machine. (Again, see Chapter 15, Equipment.)

Baking

We know several women who bake all sorts of scrumptious goodies at home and distribute them to nearby restaurants, deli's and stores. This does entail frequent trips to town, so "nearby" becomes the operative word here.

Catering

Again, this is an option for those who live near enough to a population center to make it work.

Homesteading school

Don't laugh! This is recommended only for folks who have been homesteading long enough and successfully enough to be viable teachers. The demand for this information is increasing at a rate proportional to the government's revocation of our independence and individual freedom. If the day-to-day operation of your homestead would accommodate a school, be it one day or several, it's worth thinking about. The sessions can include meals and even lodging, produce an income for you, and provide a priceless, hands-on experience for would-be homesteaders.

Alternative energy
consulting
sales, installation & service

If you are very knowledgeable in the field of alternative energy and it's application to the real world of homesteading, why not produce your income by helping others achieve independence? Design systems that best use available resources to achieve your client's needs within his/her budget, and once again, word will get around! Assuming that there are no zoning regulations to prevent it, you can operate this type of business out of your home. Depending on your location and the general interest in your area, this can be a business that is environmentally positive and profitable, as well. Here in Hawaii, where store-bought electricity costs .20/KWH, alternative energy systems have been powering a lot of homes for years and providing income to a lot of businesses that do the installations.

Child care

If any of your neighbors still work in town, and if you have the disposition and skills to look after their little ones, you can supply them a service that provides you with a steady income.

Any of the business opportunities listed above (and lots more that aren't on the list) can keep you as busy as you want to be--if you are good at what you're doing, dependable, and charge a reasonable fee for your time. Reasonable doesn't mean cheap, either. You should charge whatever the going rate is for your trade. Word spreads fast in a small community. If you are good at your craft and dependable, your reputation will find customers for you.

Being in business for yourself just beats the heck out of having a straight job. Your hours are your own, and your income is directly proportional to your effort. We've talked quite a few people into starting their own businesses, and without exception, they ended up making more money while working fewer hours than they did while at a straight job, and they had more fun. Of course, we've been very selective about whom we tried to convince. They were already self-motivated, independent folks; the kind that make good homesteaders.

Addendum

Since the first edition of this book, there has been an amazing growth in the public's use--and awareness--of the Internet. Now, there are no doubt some readers who are unhappy about my love-affair with computers (how un-homestead-like!), but my feeling is that making use of environmentally-reasonable technology is not in conflict with being a homesteader. Besides, I feel that for those families with children of any ages, it's doing them a disservice to keep them away from this technology that they will no doubt need at some time in their futures.

There's another distinct bonus to being connected to the Internet. Everything that happens on this planet is now available to each of us the instant it happens, and before the media gets a chance to "enhance" the stories with their bias. I believe this to be one of the greatest gifts bestowed upon us by modern technology. E-mail allows us instant--and free--communication with anyone on this planet, and the Internet is the most incredible, unbelievable information resource imaginable. There is no topic that you could need help with that isn't covered from numerous sources.

But this is a chapter on earning your keep, so let's get back to that. The Internet has spawned literally thousands of business opportunities in the last few years. If you make a product of offer a service, you can let the entire world know about it without having to use any of the normal and very-expensive advertising options.

The opportunities are limited only by your imagination. If you can dream up any two entities that would like to find each other, there's a business. People find long-lost family-members, a doctor in New York connects with one in California and they switch positions because each wanted to live where the other was . . . and all of these connections are made for a fee by somebody with a computer.

One enterprising man is making a small fortune selling the information on how to disable the air-bags in new cars!

I know of a woman who started a vacation-rental listing service. She charges vacation-home owners $100 a year to list with her. The home-owners are ecstatic; where else could you possibly advertise to the entire world for $100 a year? Well, after her first year, she had over 1000 listings, and all she does is add them to her Website on the Internet. The owners do the bookings. 1000 listings at $100 each per year? Do the math! The opportunities are endless!

NAILS
S.C.

When Things Look Hopeless

One Thing at a Time

The one-thing-at-a-time concept came to us one summer evening as we sat on the edge of the unfinished roof of the unfinished portion of the unfinished addition we were building onto our unfinished house. From our vantage point, we could see it all at once. Not only the house and addition, but the shop building, tank house and the greenhouse, which were all--you guessed it--unfinished.

We looked around at all the work ahead of us and were overwhelmed. We just sat there with our head in our hands and wept. We were overcome by a massive dose of depression, thinking about the thousands of hours of work required to finish just the parts we could see.

The next morning was the beginning of a new way of life for us, and we've been successfully using this method ever since. When we start the day, we decide just what we're going to accomplish before we quit for the night. We set conservative goals, too, allowing time for screw-ups and maybe even lunch.

Then during the day, the projects we have decided to do are *all* that we will do, and *all* that we will even think about. We concentrate fully on the project at hand, and if our mind wanders off to something else that needs to be done, we quickly set it back on track. It works. The projects of the day get done better and faster because each has our full attention, and at the end of the day, it's one less thing we have to think about. Done, it's history.

Even if you elect not to make it a lifestyle, the one-day-at-a-time approach is excellent therapy. If you get yourself all bummed out because of all the stuff that needs to be done, find one project that you might enjoy doing and lose yourself in it. Do nothing but that one project until it's done. When it is, you'll feel good about what you've accomplished and about yourself, and the concentration you applied for the day will clear your mind for a better and more centered day tomorrow.

You don't have to be homesteading to take one thing at a time. By keeping all things manageable, whatever you're doing, you'll take on the greatest adventure of your life.

Shift Your Attention

If the blues still seem to have you trapped, take a good look at what you're feeling. Step back and ask yourself, "Is this how I want to feel right now?" If the answer is "No," allow yourself to feel good about something else and put your attention there. For instance, if you're depressed about your broken sewer line (and we'd understand completely), fixing it is going to be torture for the entire task. But if you let go of the anguish at the horrible job before you, let your mind settle instead on your daughter's first pony ride or your son's first birthday cake--you pick your favorite image--you will find your mood lighten to the point that the task at hand becomes merely another chore.

Time to Take Off

Another pressure-release valve that should be used when appropriate is just taking off. When your work is at home, it's difficult to get away from it. Even if the workload itself isn't overwhelming, its inescapability may make it seem so. So, whether for a few hours or a few days, put everything down and get away for awhile.

If physically leaving is unpractical, find something around the place that needs to be done--that will be fun to do. For example, if you're unhappy that you're facing piling the sewer-line repair on top of the other job you were working on when you discovered the sewer line was broken, try this approach. Just walk away and find a nice, relaxing, kick-back thing to do that you can genuinely enjoy doing, but something that eventually will need to be done anyway. Like painting a porch, if you like to paint, or planting some flowers in front of the house, if that's something you like to do. There are always things to do that are a whole lot more fun than the job your "supposed to be doing." Go for it. Then when the porch looks new or the flowers are adding color to the yard, you can go back to the sewer line feeling refreshed and ready to do the repairs quickly.

Any change of pace usually does at least two things for us. It gives us a much-needed breathing space that offers us a chance to examine our priorities and goals. It also gives us a fresh perspective. When we return from any stretch of vacation or shifted attention, we always come back feeling good about diving back into the thick of whatever we're working on.

About the Authors

As a kid, Skip often asked his father why he chose to work 49 weeks of the year at a job he didn't like so that he could go up to the mountains he dearly loved for the other three weeks. He said that was how life was: a lot of sacrifice for a little pleasure.

The kid didn't buy it.

But he struggled with this dismal philosophy for years. He was somewhere in his thirties before he figured out just how wrong his father was. And in 1974, he and wife Sande moved out of the San Francisco Bay Area to the hills of Oregon. They got their feet wet in their quest for self-sufficiency by buying a rustic owner-built A-frame on four acres of woods. They heated with wood, raised almost all of their own food, and earned their keep in the shop they built on the property.

But they wanted to get farther out and really start from scratch. So in 1978, they put a down payment on 108 acres of forest on the northeast slope of Mt. Hood. The land was at 2600 feet elevation, sixteen miles from the nearest town, and there wasn't so much as a shed on it.

In the following year, they accumulated all of the materials they would need to build their cabin, mostly from old city houses that had been carefully disassembled to make room for yet another freeway.

Every time they made the trip over the mountain to their new homesite, they took as much stuff as their stout old pickup truck, with a rack to match, could hold. They made quite a few trips carrying up to 24-foot long lumber to their new homesite.

They found a great 40 year-old Case tractor with a loader, grader, and plow. Skip built a heavy-duty six-foot-wide snow plow to mount onto the loader mechanism.

Their first few years were busy and exciting. They built their cabin, shop, greenhouse, poultry house, water and electrical systems; put in a great garden, raised chickens and turkeys, and again, earned their keep right on the place. They were also successfully home-schooling their son, Jake, who was by then about six years old.

Then in June 1984, Sande died in an auto accident. Jake and his dad made do for a little over a year, and then late in 1985, Skip ran a "personals" ad in a Portland art paper looking for some possible female companionship. He wasn't looking for a wife; just a compatible lady with whom he could share some time and maybe develop a friendship. One didn't meet a lot of people living out where they did.

One of the respondents was Cathleen Freshwater, who later did become Skip's wife, friend and partner, not necessarily in that order. Cathleen had had experience in almost all of the areas of life that interested him the most, and proved to be an enthusiastic homesteading partner. Her editing expertise and their common interest in computers would later be the inspiration that started their first home-based publishing company, Oregon Wordworks.

During the next few years on the mountain, they totally debugged their electrical system. Visiting friends had a difficult time believing that they made their own electricity; they had all the electrical gadgets found in most city homes, and then some. They ran their home, shop and office with that system, never had a blackout, and the cost of operation was next to nothing.

After listening to repeated requests that they write a manual on how to duplicate their electrical system, they finally did. They self-published their first book, *More Power to You!*.

Skip, Cathleen, and Jake have always loved the ocean. They made countless trips to the beach from the mountain. During 1988 and '89, they started going to the beach at least once a month. Soon they were going every two weeks. When their trips became even more frequent, they decided that they were ready for a change, and they put the homestead up for sale.

With the proceeds from the sale of their place on the mountain, they paid off what they still owed on the land, and made a down-payment on a little house at the beach on the Oregon coast. Their intent was to stay in that house until they found just the right spot on the coast to start over with a brand-new homestead. They built an addition to house the Oregon Wordworks office, and while Cathleen ran that business, Skip started a construction company. Over the next four years, they published a newspaper and two more books, and built (and sold) four houses and remodeled two, including the house they were living in.

Meanwhile, they were warily observing the changes happening to the Oregon coast. Their once-sleepy little community was discovered by affluent city-dwellers looking for tax-deductible second homes. During their four years there, the number of homes doubled, the price of real estate tripled, and, for them anyway, the charm began to evaporate. And if that weren't enough, the timber business--which includes both government and private interests--continued to rape the forests of Oregon to the point where much of the reason for moving there was lost forever.

They started looking for other options. Knowing that they were going to have to find another destination for their next home, they started to analyze their priorities. They had moved to the coast to be near the ocean; they wanted to stay near the ocean. They loved to play in the water, so a warmer ocean would be even better. They loved lush forests, low population density, warm weather, and a laid-back lifestyle. It didn't take them a whole lot of research to focus on the Island of Hawaii. In August of 1993, they sold their little home at the beach, had a huge garage sale and packed everything that was left into a 24' container, and moved to Hawaii. Once again, they were in a little temporary house, this time in a fantastic tropical forest. And, once again, looking for that perfect spot to build their homestead, not far from where they were.

But then, in late 1994, Cathleen decided that she no longer wanted to be married, and she rode off into the sunset. Jake is now 21 and has embarked upon a thriving career in computers, and his job takes him back and forth between California and England, with occasional stops in Hawaii. Skip's plans remain, for the most part, unchanged.

In addition to several books, Skip has written numerous articles for various publications, including Backwoods Home Magazine, Back Home Magazine, Mother Earth News, and others.

This second and updated printing of *The Modern Homestead Manual* was published by Oregon Wordworks, which is still alive and well in Portland, Oregon.

Resource Guide

(See Index for specific entries.)

Alternative Energy

(See also "Books" Heading)

Trace Engineering

High-efficiency inverters.

(360) 435-8826
To locate your nearest Trace distributor: tracesales@seanet.com
For Trace literature: inverters@traceengineering.com
Website: http://www.traceengineering.com/

Solar Depot

8605-B Folsom Blvd.
Sacramento, CA 95826
(916) 381-0235
1-800-321-0101

61 Paul Drive
San Rafael, CA94903
(415) 499-1333
1-800-822-4041

Website: http://www.solardepot.com/

Complete alternative electrical inventory. Solar Depot offers a complete catalog that fully describes all products. Everything you need to build a complete system, plus the peripherals (Lights, fans, water heaters, pumps, etc.) They also offer complete packages custom designed to meet your needs.

Real Goods Trading Company

555 Leslie Street
Ukiah, CA 95482-5576
Tel: 1-800-762-7325
Fax: 1-800-508-2342
Email: realgood@realgoods.com
Website: http://www.realgoods.com/

Complete alternative electrical inventory. These folks carry every component you need to build a complete solar or small-hydro electrical system. Their catalog is a valuable resource in that it includes system-design guidelines and explains the function and operation of all of their equipment.

Sunelco, Inc., The Sun electric Company

100 Skeels Street,
P.O.Box 1499, Hamilton, Montana 59840-1499
406.363.6924
Website: http://www.sunelco.com/

Planning Guide & Product Catalog. This is much more than just a product catalog. It includes an introduction to the principles of solar power, details on planning your own system, interacting with existing utility company hookups, and product descriptions that are complete enough to help you decide what's right for your needs.

Radio Shack

Website: http://www.radioshack.com

Supplier of all kinds of electrical and electronics gear. There's one listed in just about every phone book in the country. A radio shack catalog (the big one; not a sale flyer) is a good addition to your resource library. We recommend that use of Radio Shack products be limited to parts and supplies (relays, switches, circuit boards and boxes, etc.).

China Diesel Imports

15749 Lyons Valley Road
Jamul, CA 92035
(619) 669-1995
E-mail for literature: CDI@chinadiesel.com
Website: http://www.chinadiesel.com

As well as being the only suppliers of CDI diesel generator sets, engines and parts, CDI is now a complete, one-stop-center for all your alternative-energy needs. They carry a huge selection of solar and wind components, and can design and furnish entire systems for your specific needs. CDI gensets are the least expensive of any commercially available units that we know of. The CDI engines are very basic, simple, low-tech, last nearly forever and easy to service.

Kubota Tractor Corporation

Website: http://www.garton-tractor.com/Product Pages/kubota.htm

Manufacturers of diesel tractors and diesel generators. Kubota's series of generators are proven machines that are suited to the homestead that requires serious, dependable power. Check your local Yellow Pages for your nearest dealer.

Onan Corporation

Manufacturers of several lines of excellent (if a bit pricey) diesel generator sets. These units enjoy an enviable reputation of reliability and are available in 3.5 to 7.5KW. Some are air-cooled and others utilize a radiator. All run at 1800 RPM. Check your Yellow Pages for the nearest Onan dealer.

Independent Living

Backwoods Home Magazine

Called "a practical journal of self-reliance," BHM is presented in a straightforward manner and covers just about all areas of homestead living. In addition to regular subscriptions, BHM offers their annual "Best of..." series, featuring the best of each year's articles all in one book. These volumes contain all of the "how to" articles and most of the other articles and editorials that appeared in the magazines. A yearly subscription of six issues is $19.95. Backwoods Home Magazine, P.O. Box 712, Gold Beach, OR 97444. E-mail: editors@backwoodshome.com
Website: hhtp://www.backwoodshome.com

Countryside & Small Stock Journal

The "other" real country magazine, Countryside has been wtih us for a long time, supporting life beyond the sidewalks. Emphasis is on small-stock raising and farm & garden issues, as well as general homesteading topics. Written by those who are doing it. Subscriptions are $18/year and may be ordered by calling 1-800-551-5691. E-mail: csymag@midway.tds.net
Website: http://www.countrysidemag.com

Bohica Concepts Alternative Reading Catalog

Be Prepared for anything and everything! Free catalog of books and magazines. Send $1.00 for postage. Bohica Concepts, PO Box 546, Dept. MHM, Randle, WA 98377
(360) 497-7075
E-mail: bohica@i-link-2.net

Tools

Whole Earth Access

This Berkeley, California based company beats just about anybody's prices on tools, their staff is competent, courteous and efficient, and they ship portable tools free in the continental U.S. To get an idea of the variety of offerings, check their ads in Fine Woodworking and Fine Homebuilding magazines. Or call for your needs. (800) 829-6300. Website: http://www.wholeearth.com/

Tool Crib of the North

Another excellent mail-order tool supplier. Every make and kind of power and hand tools available, including surveying instruments and other specialty tools. Order their catalog and/or watch their ads in magazines like Fine Homebuilding. P.O.Box 13720, Grand Forks, ND 58208-3720. (800) 358-3096.

Woodworker's Supply

Mail-order supplier of all kinds of tools, equipment, hardware and supplies for the woodworker and cabinet-builder. Lots of hard-to-find hardware items and specialty tools. Ask for a catalog. 1108 North Glenn Road, Casper, Wyoming 82601. (800) 645-9292.

Cascade Tools, Inc.

Suppliers of high-quality router bits, shaper cutters and related accessories. These folks provide the professional trades with excellent products at the best prices we've found anywhere. And the service and shipping is courteous and prompt. Ask for a catalog. P.O.Box 3110, Bellingham, WA 98227. (800) 235-0272, 24 hours a day!

Grizzly Imports, Inc.

Manufacturers and importers of Woodworking shop machinery, like table saws, band saws, jointers, shapers, drill presses, etc. They have some great deals on shop-size dust-collection systems, and carry a complete line of power tool accessories, as well. Their prices are almost unbelievably low, and their products carry an excellent guarantee. They'll ship the same day you order. Ask for a catalog. Grizzly West, P.O.Box 2069, Bellingham, WA 98227, (800) 225-0021. Grizzly East, 2406 Reach Road, Williamsport, PA 17701, (800) 523-4777.

Miscellaneous Equipment

[Note: Captive-air tanks, pumps and related equipment can be found at plumbing-supply dealers and at many hardware outlets. The portable transfer pump mentioned on page 114 is Grainger's No. 1P862. The fire pump (page 117) is No. 3P636. The wonderful little 110-volt submersible pump (page 117) is No. 1P809. The high-pressure pump (pages 114 & 117) is a Sears 71AF46121N High Pressure twin-piston sprayer. 500PSI/3gpm. An alternative is their 71AF46131N roller pump, 5gpm, 150psi. Other alternatives are often available from Northern Hydraulics. Check their catalog. In-line-type water heaters (page 128) are available through most RV dealers as well as most alternative-energy stores. The brand we had such good luck with was Paloma. Water-heater timer is an Intermatic "Little Gray Box," available at most electrical-supplies dealers and some building-materials stores.]

Northern Hydraulics

P.O. Box 1499
Burnsville, MN 55337-0499
1-800-533-5545
Fax 1-612-894-0083

Pumps, compressors, electric motors, tools, small gasoline engines, hydraulic equipment, much more. Large inventory, great service, good prices on most items, but be sure to shop around. Mail/phone order. Call for free catalog to keep in your resource library.

W.W. Grainger, Inc.

Locations all over the country; consult your nearest big-city phone book. Grainger's is a good source for just about any electrical need. In addition to all sorts of electrical hardware, they carry many different kinds of fans, pumps, motors, small engines and tools. If you have difficulty locating a Grainger's branch near you, look in the yellow pages under "electrical equipment" and find someone who sells Dayton brand products (Grainger's house brand). They will probably have a catalog on hand and will be able to order anything in it for you.

For the specific model numbers of components used in this book, see the sidebar above, under the heading, "Miscellaneous Equipment."

CDI

See China Diesel Imports ("Alternative Energy" heading).

CT Farm & Family

This is an agricultural supply that carries parts for just about every tractor ever built, regardless of age. Their inventory includes engine parts, overhaul kits, completely overhauled engines, hydraulic components and an unbelievable array of parts for drive train, brake and cooling systems, and accessories. They even have new sheet metal and matching paint for vintage tractors, as well as a warehouse full of used parts. They also stock shop manuals for most tractors, a collectors' historical series (again on tractors), and some great books of interest to people who are raising small livestock and poultry. For phone orders anywhere in the 50 states and Puerto Rico, the general information number is (800) 247-7508. Their catalog is a must-have resource on any homestead.

Dennis Kirk

OK, this is for the esoteric few of us who are into motorcycles, ATV's, snowmobiles and small watercraft. This company is one of those that's an uncommon pleasure to deal with. You call their 24-hour-a-day toll-free number, and you get to talk to a bright, intelligent, efficient real person. They ship the same day and carry an amazing inventory of parts to repair, modify or uprgade your machine. They have several catalogs available, depending on your individual needs. Call (800) 328-9280 for your very own. They are located at 955 South Field Avenue, Rush City, MN 55069.

Home Business/Office/School Supplies

Computers and peripherals

This isn't actually a *specific* source, but if you find yourself in need of a computer, printer, scanner, etc., and don't exactly need the very latest and fastest equipment available, you're in luck. Most of the computer magazines have lots of ads from companies that sell "obsolete" equipment for pennies on the dollar. By "obsolete," we mean anything that's been on the market more than a few years. For example, this book was originally compiled to camera-ready status on an IBM-clone 386/33 computer. Although a 386 is now a worthless dinosaur, it's all that's necessary if you need a tool with which to write books. The bottom line: this computer will do anything we will ever expect of it, and then some. We haven't even tapped a fraction of its potential, so why buy a faster one? (We have faster computers for where we need them now, but still use the dinosaur for writing books!)

Another excellent way to acquire a computer is to buy used out of your newspaper classified ads. We paid about $2500 for this machine, and it would be hard to *give* it away today!. We often see real bargains in ads in the paper for used computers, complete with printers and tons of software. If you have a problem with buying used stuff, you can also wheel and deal with computer dealers in your nearest big town. There is very little market for last year's equipment, so don't take the asking price very seriously.

If you're going to do any kind of work that needs to look good (as opposed to bookkeeping chores and the like), buy a laser printer right up front. You're going to need one sooner or later anyway, so why not now? The prices have come way down in the last few years on these too. If you wish to pursue this further, see Backwoods Home Magazine, Issue no. 11 (Sept./Oct., 1991).

We do offer one excellent supplier for refurbished computer equipment and peripherals, though, and that's Surplus Direct in Oregon. Their phone: (800)753-7877. Website: http://www.surplusdirect.com/

Viking Office Products

This is an excellent resource for those folks who don't live near an Office Depot, Office Max, or some similar mega-outlet of office supplies. These folks have the best prices we've found on an absolutely amazing inventory of anything you could ever need in an office and on a lot of school supplies, including computer supplies and peripherals and even office furniture. They ship anywhere in the country, and on orders over $25, the shipping is free! The service is amazing, too. We receive our shipments no later than two days after the order was placed, and any time there's an error in the shipment, be it yours or theirs, they'll send UPS to come pick up the item(s) in question, and they pay the freight. The only catch is you have to have a business name, which shouldn't be much of a problem if you need supplies for your office or home-school. Ask for a catalog. (800) 421-1222. Toll-free Fax order line is (800) 762-7329.

Dale Seymour Publications

Classroom posters of every imaginable description. Mathematics, fine arts, science, language arts, visual thinking, history, and more. There are three catalogs available: "Classroom Posters," "General K-8 Catalog," and the "Secondary Mathematics Catalog." Office and Warehouse: 1100 Hamilton Court, Menlo Park, CA94025. (800) 872-1100.

Books

More Power To You, by Skip Thomsen. ISBN: 0-9625960-3-5.

A step-by-step manual describing the electrical power system which operated the author's wilderness home for over ten years without a hitch. The fully-evolved version was built around a China Diesel generator, and supplied the home, office, and shop with 'round the clock 110-volt power and daytime 220. The book also includes instructions for building remote-control systems, constructing a sound-proof generator shed, and maintaining, servicing, and trouble-shooting.

Order direct from Oregon Wordworks,P.O. Box 231091, Portland, OR 97281. Price is $9.95 plus $2 S&H from the publisher, or may be ordered through your local book store. You may also order from the Oregon Wordworks Website: http://www.mailbooks.com

A Relay Primer, by Skip Thomsen. ISBN: 0-9625960-1-9.

A Relay Primer is a companion booklet to *More Power To You!*. In lay terminology, it describes the construction, operation and uses of electrical relays, which are used extensively in power-systems in general and in their remote-control systems in particular. It is designed for those who have a general working knowledge of how electrical systems work but are fuzzy on the operation of relays.

Order direct from Oregon Wordworks, P.O. Box 231091, Portland, OR 97281. Price is $3.95 postpaid from the publisher, or may be ordered through your local book store. You may also order from the Oregon Wordworks Website: http://www.mailbooks.com

A Graphic guide to Frame Construction, by Rob Thallon. ISBN 1-56158-040-6.

This book covers every detail from the very beginning of the project to the very end, and supports the clear and concise text with excellent drawings. The book is thoughtfully arranged and well indexed, making it a snap to find even the most obscure detail.

It is available for $29.95 from The Taunton Press, Inc. (publishers of Fine Homebuilding), Box 5506, Newtown, CT 06470-5506. Or from your nearest bookstore.

Electrical Wiring, by Thomas S. Colvin.

Excellent manual covering all phases of residential wiring. Very clearly written text supported by well-presented drawings and diagrams. Everything the layman needs to wire his own house, and a lot of information useful to the experienced builder, too.

Published by The American Association for Vocational Instructional Materials, 220 Smithonia Road, Winterville, Georgia 30683. ISBN 0-89606-302-X. Can be ordered directly from AAVIM by calling (706) 742-5355.

Planning for an Individual Water System.

Covers all phases of individual water systems. Very clearly written text supported by well-presented drawings and diagrams. Everything you need to design and build your own water system, regardless of the source of the water.

Published by The American Association for Vocational Instructional Materials, 220 Smithonia Road, Winterville, Georgia 30683. ISBN 0-89606-097-7. Can be ordered directly from AAVIM by calling (706) 742-5355.

Making Kitchen Cabinets, by Paul Levine.

Detailed instructions and photos covering Eurostyle cabinets and whole-kitchen planning, too. Available from Taunton Press, Inc. (publishers of *Fine Homebuilding*), Box 5506, Newtown, CT 06470-5506.

Building Your Own Kitchen Cabinets, by Jere Cary.

Complete guide to designing and building traditional cabinets. Available from Taunton Press, Inc. (publishers of *Fine Homebuilding*), Box 5506, Newtown, CT 06470-5506.

Ponds-Planning, Design, Construction, USDA Soil conservation Service, Agricultural Handbook #590.

A complete reference on preliminary site investigations, how to estimate runoff, all aspects of building embankment and excavated ponds, sealing the pond, and finally, protecting and maintaining your finished pond.

Unfortunately, this fine reference is out of print. About the only source at this point is your nearest office of the USDA Soil conservation Service, and if they don't have any left for sale, they might at least be able to loan you one.

Kids & Home Schooling

Country Kids by Julie Kendrick. ISBN: 0-914400-22-3.

Long out of print, this book is worth the effort to find at the library. Another possible source would be the personal library of someone who was raising country kids in the early seventies. This book covers traditional and experimental lifestyles, the effects of isolation, rural educational systems, recreation without the "served-up" recreactional facilities found in most cities, and rural health care (including childbirth).

Summerhill School, A new View of Childhood by A. S. Neill, St. Martin's Press, edited by Albert Lamb. ISBN: 0-312-08860-4.

Originally written about in 1960, Summerhill, a Radical Approach to Child Rearing caused a furor around the world. Rewritten for the 90's, Summerhill School still proposes the best approach to raising self-confident and emotionally healthy children. Summerhill's techniques are easily applied in the home.

How to Talk So Kids Will Listen & Listen So Kids Will Talk by Adele Faber and Elaine Mazlish, Avon Books. ISBN: 0-380-57000-9.

A collection of exercises to open up and enrich communication between parents and children, and anyone else with whom you wish to apply the techniques. Easy and fun to read with whimsical illustrations by Kimberly Ann Coe.

Legal Services

HALT, An Organization of Americans for Legal Reform

is a national non-partisan public-interest group that is dedicated to increasing awareness that people can--and should be able to--handle their own civil legal affairs. To that end, HALT publishes a number of "legal manuals," written in easy-to-understand language. Each contains "how-to" information and lists of other resources and explanations of the law and citizen's rights and responsibilities. One particularly helpful manual is called "Real Estate--Buying a House or Condo," and contains just everything you will ever need to know about buying and/or selling a piece of real estate with little or no outside help. Other manuals include topics like shopping for and using a lawyer, small claims court procedures, estate planning, and more. You can order direct, ask for a list of current publications or get more information by calling HALT, Inc., (202) 347-9600. The address is 1319 F Street NW, Suite 300, Washington, D.C. 20004.

Nolo Press, Self-help Law books and Software

The leading publisher of self-help law books and software since 1971. Nolo Press was started by two Legal Aid lawyers who were fed up with the fact that the average person couldn't find affordable legal information and advice. Convinced that with good, reliable information, Americans could handle routine legal problems without hiring an attorney, they began writing plain-English law books for non-lawyers.

Now, twenty-seven years later, Nolo Press publishes more than 120 titles--books, software, legal forms, audio and video tapes. With over five million copies in print, our products have helped more people take care of their legal work than any lawyer or law firm in history.

These folks have got do-it-yourself books for just about every conceivable legal matter and each is especially prepared for the appropriate State. We've been using their books and software for years. Their Website has tons of information, plus a terrific section devoted just to lawyer jokes! They even have a sense of humor! (Contact info next page...)

Nolo Press , continued

To order by phone: 1-800-992-6656
Customer Service: 1-800-728-3555, Monday-Friday, 9am-5pm - Pacific Time.
E-mail: cs@nolo.com
Mailing Address:
Nolo Press
950 Parker Street
Berkeley, CA 94710
Website: http://www.nolo.com/

Miscellaneous

A Source of Inner Peace

Perhaps this is stepping a little bit off the direct path to successful homesteading, but to this homesteader/ author it is the direct path to a successful life. After that, everything else is easy. The writings of Eknath Eswaren, writings that apply as well to any discipline or religious faith, are my source of inspiration and inner peace. I feel they apply especially well to those of us who are consciously working on our own self-reliance . . . as in Homesteaders! I recommend them to all.

My favorite of his many books is Conquest of Mind (ISBN 0-915132-50-8), available from Nilgiri Press, Box 256, Tomales, CA 94971, or any of his books may be ordered at any book store.

A Pattern Language, ISBN 0-19-501919-9

This is another book that we didn't list in the "books" section, simply because it's too special and esoteric to be listed there with all the how-to stuff. This one is for the person who is designing--or even contemplating deigning--that perfect home, homestead or even community, in which everything works in synergy with everything else, including the human element . . . perfect harmony.

From the book jacket, "At the core of the book is the point that in designing their environments people always rely on certain "languages," which, like the languages we speak, allow them to articulate and communicate an infinite variety of designs within a formal system which gives them coherence.

"This book provides a language of this kind. It will enable a person to make a design for almost any kind of building, or any part of the built environment.

" Patterns, the units of this language, are answers to design problems (How high should a window sill be? How many stories should a building have? How much space in a neighborhood should be devoted to grass and trees?). More than 250 of the patterns are given; each consists of a problem statement, a discussion of the problem with an illustration, and a solution. ....many of the patterns are archetypal, so deeply rooted in the nature of things that it seems likely that they will be a part of human nature, and human action, as much in five hundred years as they are today."

OK, it's a bit heavy on the philosophy, but it is deeply interesting reading to anyone who truly appreciates the sensitive and conscious design of environments.

(It's a bit pricey, so you might want to get this one from the library!)

Index

(* refers to entries in the Resource Guide.)

accounting 186
adult education 27,187
alternative energy 73,77-98,108,110,113,115-117,125,127,130,188,199-201*
antique stoves 176-178
appraisals, real estate 57
arts and crafts 16,186
auctions 25,27,155
auto insurance 165,168
baking 187
bartering 13,47
basic rules 7,9,43,60,81,144,152
batteries 78,79,81,84,85,87,91,92,96,110,112,127,158,199*,200*
blue prints 67
bookkeeping 186
books 208 *
booster pumps 111,116,123,125,126,204-5*
building codes 36,65,130-1
building contractors 67,69-70
building inspection 57-8,66,69,73-5
building materials 17,24-6,39,69,73,151
building officials 26,66
building, road 17,72,148,161
bulldozers 71,159,161-2,187
bureaucrats 26,35,36,66,77
business opportunities 8,16,183-9
buying equipment 24-5,151-162
cabinet building 209*
capital 7,14,43
captive-air tanks 117,119,120
carpentry 27,155,185
cash reserves 14-5
catchment 32,104,109,125
catering 187
CB radio 48
centrifugal pumps 114-5,204*
cheap tools 24-5,75,152-6
chicken-spit 140
child care 188
children 3,8,16,33,43,49,51-4,142,148,161,179, 188, 210*
cisterns 101,103,104,108,109,114,123
classifieds 9,24,27,155,157,168
clearing, land 161
coal-burning stoves 177
codes, building 36,65-7,130-1
common sense 3,27,51,144
communication 48,209
compressors 202-5*
computer peripherals 206-7*
concrete 57,73,185
confidence 3,27,52,209
contingencies 60-1
contractors, building 67,69-70
contractors, electrical 73-4
contractors, plumbing 73-4
contracts 19-20,60-1
cook stoves 177
covenants 34
crafts 16,186
decisions 14,23,31,36,78,111,162,166
deep well pumps 104,111,204*
depreciation,19-20
depression 191-3
design, house 26,36,57,65-7
desktop publishing 27,184
destination 31-6
diesel engine generators 84,85-6,92-8,158-9,171,206*
disclosures 34-5
discount tools 154
diversity 24
dozers 71,159,161,162,187
dream, the 4,24
easements 67
economy cars 165
education 1,3,27,31,33,53-4,187-8
education, adult 27,187
electric motors 204-5*
electrical contractors 73-4
electrical hardware 199-200*,204*
electrical inspection 69,74-5
electrical wiring 210*
engines, small 204-5*
equipment 151-163
equipment, buying 24,25,151-162
equipment, farm 156-9
equipment, miscellaneous 204-6*
equipment, moving 39-41
equipment, solar 199-200*
equipment, snow-removal 17,159-60
evening schools 27,187
farm equipment 156-9

farming 156
finances 8,14,18,57
fine print 61-2,175
fire insurance 118
fire pumps 111,117-8,204-5*
firewood 47,149,153,157,175
float switch 122
foundations 69,72-3,130-1
four-wheel drive 142,158,165,170
freedom 1,3-4,13,66,140,142,187
front-wheel drive 170
furniture, manufacturing 185
gas generators 81-6,89,91
gas-engine pumps 112,204-5*
generator-welders 83
generators 77-88, 201*
generators, diesel 84,85-6,92-8,158-9, 171, 201*
generators, gas 81-6,89,91
generators, hydro-electric 77
generators, portable 90,116
generators, RV 83
generators, wind 79
government 1,34,65,148
hardware, electrical 199-200*,204*
hauling water 104,108,133-5,142,147
heat tape 131
heating 63,78,95,130,133,175-81
heavy-equipment operating 71,162,186-7
hippies 9,13,47
home business 183-9,206-7*
home schooling 3,33,43,51,53-4, 210*
homeowners insurance 14,17,19,118
hopelessness 191-2
house design 65
house plans 67
hydro-electric generators 77
income 14-21,25,40,141,143,144,146,161, 183-9
independence 2,16,47,165,183,188
inspection, building 57,58,66,69,73-5
inspection, electrical 69,74-5
inspection, plumbing 69,74-5
inspections, house 57-9
insurance 13,14,17,118,165,168
insurance, auto 165,168
insurance, fire 118
insurance, homeowners 14,17,19,118
inverters 72,78,81,84-5,87,91,96-7,104,110-1, 113,116,117,123,126,127,199*
IRS 13-4,19-20
jet pumps 104,204*
jobs,4,13,16-7,27,28,69,156,161,183-9
Joneses, the 52
kids 3,8,16,33,43,49,51-4,142,148,161,179, 188, 210*
land clearing 161
legal services 211*
loans 61-3
lumber 14,26
lumber yards 26,101
maintenance20,63,78,79,83,90,115,153,171-2, 177
manufacturing furniture 185
materials storage 40-2
miscellaneous equipment 199-201*, 204-205*
money 13-21,41,43,57,60,141,143-6,156,159, 167,170,189
mortgage 19,21
motors, electric 204-5*
moving equipment 39-41
moving 39-44
moving van 40-1,134
music 52
neighbors 3-4,23,31-6,40,47-9,51,81,84, 106,188
newspapers 2,23-4,27,155,184
office supplies 206-7*
operating, heavy equipment 71,162,186-7
owner-builder 67,70,73
partners 7-11
pellet stoves 175
permits 35,36,61,65,67-9,72,74
personals ads 9-10
phantom loads 84
philosophy 1,140
pickups 165,169-70
planning 7,15,31-6
plumbers 72-5
plumbing57,59,68,73,75,101,128-9,130
plumbing contractors 68,69,73,75
plumbing inspection 74
plumbing insulation 130-2
politics 31,34,35,140
ponds 109-10, 209*
portable generator 90, 116, 199-201*
portable pumps 114, 115, 204*
power tools 72,74,79,152-5
pressure tanks 103,108,117,119,120,204*
property taxes 14,17,18
public schools 1,33,54
publishing, desktop 27, 184, 206-7*
pump noise 122
pumps 104,110-4,204-5*
pumps, 12-volt 111-2,199-200*
pumps, booster 111,204-5*
pumps, deep well 108,111,113-4,204-5*
pumps, fire 111,117-8,204-5*
pumps, gas-engine 112,204-5*

pumps, jet 104,204-5*
pumps, portable 114,115,136*,204-5*
pumps, shallow well 104,110,204-5*
pumps, submersible 104,110,204-5*
pumps, transfer 111,112,114-5,136,204-5*
quarters, temporary 43
ranching 145
realtors 34,59-61
rednecks 47
remodeled houses 43,59,155,185
rental 18-21
repair business 184,185,186
research 23,27,40,66,152,166
responsibility 3, 4, 51, 213*
retirement income 18-9
road building 17,22,148,161
rules, basic 7,9,43,60,81,144,152
rural properties 19,61
RV generators 83
Saturday market 16,186
school 31,33,43,51,53-4
self-confidence 3, 4, 27, 52, 213*
self-reliance 1-5
self-sufficiency 15,18,27,39,80,183-9
setbacks 67
sewing 16,27,186
shallow well pumps 104,111,204-5*
skills 2,7,27-8,43,52,69,161,172
small engines 204-5*
snow removal equipment 17,159-60
snow plow 17,47,158
solar 72,86-7
solar equipment 199-200*
solar systems 77-80
springs 101,103-5,108-10,112,115,123
storage, materials 40-2
storage, water 32,104-5,108-9,115, 121,123,125
stove repair 175-8
stoves, antique 176-8
stoves, coal-burning 177
stoves, cook 177
stoves, pellet 175
stoves, wood 175-81
streams 77,101,115,121,125
subcontractors 69-74
submersible pumps 104,204-5*
subscriptions 2,23-4,202*
Summerhill School 210*
surge tank 117,204-5*
systems, electrical 77-87,89-98
systems, water 101-36
tankless water heaters 112,128-9,136, 199-200*
tanks, water storage 32,104,105,108-10,112, 115,123
tanks, captive-air 117,119,120,204*
tanks, pressure 103,108,117,119,120,204*
television 2,52
temporary quarters 42-4
time off 192
tires 167-8
togetherness 7-11
tool resources 152-3,202-5*
tool warranties 153-4
tools 203-5*
tools, 12-volt 87,155,199-200*
tools, cheap 24,25,75,152-6
tools, discount 154
tools, power 152-5
tractor parts 205*
tractor work 186
tractors 157-9
trailers 39,43,162,168-9
transfer pumps 111,112,114-5,136,204-5*
trucks 39-40,108,133-6,165-7,170
12-volt pumps 111,112
12-volt tools 87,155,199-200*
UBC (Uniform Building Code) 66
undercapitalization 7,14
Uniform Building Code (UBC) 66
vacation 192
van, moving 40-1,134
vans 166
vehicles 87,142,165-72
warranties 89,153,157
water, availability of 104-6
water heater timer 127,136,204*
water heaters 112,125,127-8
water heaters, tankless 128-9,199-200*
water storage 108-10
water systems 101-36
water truck 133-6
weather 2,31-2,43,48,78,93,430-2,147,169
welder-generators 83
welding 27,82,185
wells 103-8
wind generators 79
wiring 57-8, 68, 72-3, 113, 209*
wood stoves 175-81